60p.

**REVISE BTEC**

# Information and
# Creative Technology

ibrary: 0115 884263
alno... m.ac

**Unit 1 The Online World**
**Unit 2 Technology Systems**

# REVISION
# WORKBOOK

Series Consultant: Harry Smith

Author: Karen Anderson

- - - - - - - - - - - - - - - - - - - - - - - - - - - - - - - - - - - - - - - - - - - -

## A note from the publisher

In order to ensure that this resource offers high-quality support for the associated Pearson qualification, it has been through a review process by the awarding body. This process confirms that; this resource fully covers the teaching and learning content of the specification or part of a specification at which it is aimed. It also confirms that it demonstrates an appropriate balance between the development of subject skills, knowledge and understanding, in addition to preparation for assessment.

Endorsement does not cover any guidance on assessment activities or processes (e.g. practice questions or advice on how to answer assessment questions), included in the resource nor does it prescribe any particular approach to the teaching or delivery of a related course.

While the publishers have made every attempt to ensure that advice on the qualification and its assessment

is accurate, the official specification and associated assessment guidance materials are the only authoritative source of information and should always be referred to for definitive guidance.

Pearson examiners have not contributed to any sections in this resource relevant to examination papers for which they have responsibility.

Examiners will not use endorsed resources as a source of material for any assessment set by Pearson.

Endorsement of a resource does not mean that the resource is required to achieve this Pearson qualification, nor does it mean that it is the only suitable material available to support the qualification, and any resource lists produced by the awarding body shall include this and other appropriate resources.

**For the full range of Pearson revision titles across GCSE, BTEC and AS/A Level visit:**
**www.pearsonschools.co.uk/revise**

Published by Pearson Education Limited, 80 Strand, London, WC2R 0RL

www.pearsonschoolsandfecolleges.co.uk

Copies of official specifications for all Pearson qualifications may be found on the website: www.edexcel.com

Text © Pearson Education Limited 2014
Typeset by Tech-Set Ltd, Gateshead
Original illustrations © Pearson Education Limited
Cover photo/illustration by Miriam Sturdee

The right of Karen Anderson to be identified as the author of this work have been asserted by her in accordance with the Copyright, Designs and Patents Act 1988.

First published 2014

17 16 15
10 9 8 7 6 5 4 3 2

**British Library Cataloguing in Publication Data**
A catalogue record for this book is available from the British Library

ISBN 978 1 446 90980 5

Printed in Slovakia by Neografia

**Acknowledgements**

The publisher would like to thank the following for their kind permission to reproduce their photographs:

(Key: b-bottom; c-centre; l-left; r-right; t-top)

**Shutterstock.com:** Masalski Maksim 41 (c), supergenijalac 43c; **Veer / Corbis:** Kitch 42t, LCS 41 (a), Ronen 41 (d), StockPhotosArt.com 41 (b)

All other images © Pearson Education

Every effort has been made to trace the copyright holders and we apologise in advance for any unintentional omissions. We would be pleased to insert the appropriate acknowledgement in any subsequent edition of this publication.

**A note from the publisher**

In order to ensure that this resource offers high-quality support for the associated BTEC qualification, it has been through a review process by the awarding body to confirm that it fully covers the teaching and learning content of the specification or part of a specification at which it is aimed, and demonstrates an appropriate balance between the development of subject skills, knowledge and understanding, in addition to preparation for assessment.

While the publishers have made every attempt to ensure that advice on the qualification and its assessment is accurate, the official specification and associated assessment guidance materials are the only authoritative source of information and should always be referred to for definitive guidance.

BTEC examiners have not contributed to any sections in this resource relevant to examination papers for which they have responsibility.

No material from an endorsed book will be used verbatim in any assessment set by BTEC.

Endorsement of a book does not mean that the book is required to achieve this BTEC qualification, nor does it mean that it is the only suitable material available to support the qualification, and any resource lists produced by the awarding body shall include this and other appropriate resources.

# Contents

This book covers the externally assessed units in the BTEC Level 1/Level 2 First in Information and Creative Technology qualification.

Pearson publishes Sample Assessment Material and the Specification on its website. That is the official content, and this book should be used in conjunction with it. The questions in this book have been written to help you practise what you have learned in your revision. Remember: The real test questions may not look like this.

 **Guided**   These questions provide part of a model answer to help you get started.

# Online services 1

**1** 

Which **one** of these is a government online service? **(1 mark)**

A ☐ Internet banking

B ☐ Train timetables

C ☐ Online auction sites

D ☒ Online tax returns

**2**

Give **one** example of a real-time online service and explain why it is real-time. **(2 marks)**

> Think carefully about the explanation you give here.

Airlines

live up to date info

..........................................................................................

..........................................................................................

..........................................................................................

> **Guided**

**3**

Using **two** examples, describe what types of online services can be described as commerce. **(4 marks)**

Commerce online services involve money. One example of an online commerce service is a retail website where products are sold over the internet, such as ...........................................

..........................................................................................

..........................................................................................

Another example is ....................................................................................

..........................................................................................

**4**

What type of online service is email? **(1 mark)**

A ☐ Communication    B ☐ Real-time

C ☐ Commerce          D ☐ Government

# Online services 2

**Guided** **1**

> What is a VLE? **(3 marks)**

VLE stands for ...............................................................................................................................

It is used in schools and colleges by both teachers and students.

................................................................

> Go on to describe how it is used by both categories of people.

........................................................................................................................................................

........................................................................................................................................................

**2**

> State **two** types of files which can be accessed by online download services. **(2 marks)**

........................................................................................................................................................

........................................................................................................................................................

**3**

> Which **one** of these is not an online entertainment service? **(1 mark)**

**A** ☐ Video conferencing

**B** ☐ Online gaming

> Notice the negative in the question – make sure you read all questions carefully!

**C** ☐ On demand films

**D** ☐ Radio player

**4**

> Match each sector to **two** appropriate examples of an online service. **(2 marks)**

| Education |
| --- |
| Business |

| Online learning |
| --- |
| Video conferencing |
| Virtual learning environment |
| Internet banking |

# Online advertising

**1**

Which **one** of these is a type of online advertising?  **(1 mark)**

A ☐  Pay-per-view

B ☐  Pay-per-click

C ☐  Pay-per-page

D ☐  Pay-per-ad

**2**  A business can pay for sponsored links in search results for particular key words.

Explain why a business might pay for this service.  **(2 marks)**

..................................................................................................................................................

..................................................................................................................................................

**3**

Explain why pop-up adverts might be annoying to internet users.  **(2 marks)**

Think about why they have this unintended effect on some people.

..................................................................................................................................................

..................................................................................................................................................

..................................................................................................................................................

..................................................................................................................................................

..................................................................................................................................................

**Guided**  **4**  Businesses have a limited budget for marketing. They need to choose how much to spend on offline and online advertising.

Describe **two** ways a business can advertise online and explain why it might choose this method of promotion.  **(6 marks)**

Methods of online advertising include banner adverts, pop-up adverts, ...........................................

..................................................................................................................................................

..................................................................................................................................................

..................................................................................................................................................

..................................................................................................................................................

..................................................................................................................................................

# Online documents – file compression

**1**

> Which **one** of these is another name for compressing files? **(1 mark)**

**A** ☐ Lacing

**B** ☐ Fastening

**C** ☐ Zipping

**D** ☐ Buttoning

**2** Anya needs to email a large file to her colleague.

> Give **one** reason why you might advise her to compress her file. **(2 marks)**

> It asks for one reason but is for two marks – so you need to explain your reason.

..............................

.................................................................................................................................

.................................................................................................................................

.................................................................................................................................

.................................................................................................................................

**Guided** **3**

> Explain how a file is compressed and decompressed. **(2 marks)**

> This question needs you to explain the process in sequence. Make sure you include technical terminology.

A file is compressed using an ...........................................................................................

.................................................................................................................................

.................................................................................................................................

**4** Jenny has taken a video of her friend playing football at school. The file limit is 1.2GB, and her memory stick is 1GB. She needs to save it to her memory stick so she can take it with her.

> Explain two ways in which she can make the file fit. **(2 marks)**

.................................................................................................................................

.................................................................................................................................

.................................................................................................................................

.................................................................................................................................

# Online software and backups

1   Online software will usually backup files automatically. What is a backup?   **(1 mark)**

........................................................................................................................................

2   What is the main difference between standalone software and online software?   **(2 marks)**

........................................................................................................................................

........................................................................................................................................

3   Reha runs a secretarial business and is considering using only online software with her team.

**(a)** Describe **two** advantages of this.   **(4 marks)**

..............................................................................   │ You have been given a scenario – use
..............................................................................   │ this in your answer to justify your ideas.

........................................................................................................................................

........................................................................................................................................

........................................................................................................................................

........................................................................................................................................

........................................................................................................................................

........................................................................................................................................

**Guided**   You want to present Reha with a balanced view.

**(b)** Describe **two** risks of her moving to using only online software.   **(4 marks)**

One risk is security, ....................................................................................................................

........................................................................................................................................

Another risk is reliance on an external company, ............................................................................

........................................................................................................................................

> You will need to use your knowledge
> of all online services to help you
> answer this question.

# Collaborative working online

1

> State **one** reason why version control is important for those working collaboratively on a document. **(1 mark)**

..................................................................................................................................

**Guided** 2  Saleem works in a business which has branches all over the world. He needs to work on a project with colleagues in a different country.

> Describe an advantage of using online collaborative working tools. **(2 marks)**

Collaborative working tools can be accessed ...........................................................................

..................................................................................................................................

..................................................................................................................................

3  Brandon is a receptionist in a car sales showroom, Lydia is a salesperson and Shaheeb is the owner. They each have different levels of access to their customer records.

> **(a)** Complete the table below. **(4 marks)**

| Person | Level of access | Actions allowed |
|--------|-----------------|-----------------|
| Brandon | Read-only | Can view the customer records but not edit them |
| Lydia | | |
| Shaheeb | | |

> The first row has been given for you – use this pattern to complete the other two rows.

Brandon needs to have read-write access to the salespeople's calendars so he can book in appointments with customers. He has just started working at the company this week.

> **(b)** What should he receive before being given this level of access? **(1 mark)**

..................................................................................................................................

# Online communication 1

**1**

> Who can edit a wiki? **(1 mark)**

**A** ☐ Anyone

**B** ☑ Members of the wiki (people who have signed up)

**C** ☐ The owner of the wiki only

**D** ☐ No-one

**2**

> Select the correct definition for these two terms. **(2 marks)**

> Draw a line between the term and the correct definition. You only need to select one definition for each.

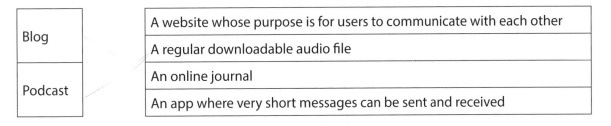

| | |
|---|---|
| Blog | A website whose purpose is for users to communicate with each other |
| | A regular downloadable audio file |
| | An online journal |
| Podcast | An app where very short messages can be sent and received |

**3** Users of an online chatroom need to be present at the same time in order to take part. Users of an online forum do not need to be present at the same time in order to take part.

> Explain this by giving **one** benefit for each. **(2 marks)**

......................................................................................................................................

......................................................................................................................................

**4**

> **(a)** What is an online community? **(2 marks)**

......................................................................................

......................................................................................

......................................................................................

......................................................................................

> This question asks for a definition and it is worth two marks. You do not need to give an example.

A business that sells using e-commerce wants to build an online community.

> **(b)** Give **one** example of a method it might use and **one** reason why this may benefit the business. **(2 marks)**

......................................................................................................................................

......................................................................................................................................

# Online communication 2

**1**

> Which **one** of these is not good netiquette?     **(1 mark)**

**A** ☐ Using emoticons

**B** ☐ Typing in capitals

**C** ☐ Having an avatar

**D** ☐ Using abbreviations like lol and brb

**2**

> Identify the **three** labelled sections of this example of instant messaging.     **(3 marks)**

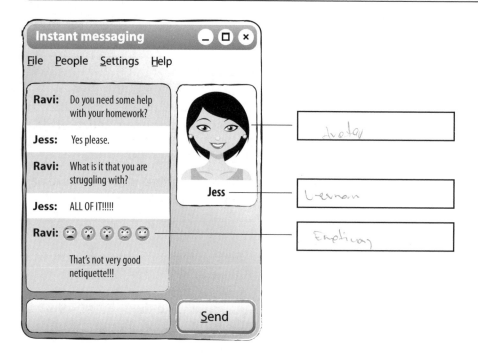

avatar

Username

Emoticon

**3** The table below shows three details which may be given on a social networking profile.

> Explain why these might not be truthful and how that may be a risk.     **(3 marks)**

| Username | JohnnySmith | |
| --- | --- | --- |
| Age | 14 | |
| Location | \<the same region as you\> | |

# Voice over Internet Protocol

**1**

What information directs VoIP (Voice over Internet Protocol) data to the correct computer? An example would be 125.76.23.003. **(1 mark)**

**A** ☐ MAC address

**B** ☐ Username

**C** ☐ Codec

**D** ☐ IP address

**2**

State **two** types of data sent using VoIP. **(2 marks)**

Voice

Longva view

**3**

Name two pieces of equipment that are used to record a VoIP message. **(2 marks)**

Internet connection

Device

**Guided** **4**

Discuss why VoIP might be used by a business, describing advantages and disadvantages. **(8 marks)**

VoIP can be used in businesses to hold meetings with employees at branches in different

countries. An advantage of this is ........................................................................................

..............................................................................................................................................

..............................................................................................................................................

Another way VoIP can be used in business is for collaborative working, which is .....................

..............................................................................................................................................

..............................................................................................................................................

..............................................................................................................................................

Consider how you will structure your answer, based on the 8 marks available. You could describe two uses, two advantages and two disadvantages. Alternatively you could describe a use and associated advantage and disadvantage and another use, advantage and disadvantage.

# Cloud computing

1 | Where is data stored in cloud computing? | (1 mark)

A ☐ Internal servers

B ☒ External servers

C ☐ External drives

D ☐ Internal drives

2 | Identify **two** types of software that can be used to access the cloud. | (2 marks)

..........................................................................................................................................................

..........................................................................................................................................................

.................................................................................

> Think about the types of devices you might use to access the cloud.

..................................................................

3 Tony is a sales representative for a design company. He travels to clients around the UK and needs to access company customer records and files of designs.

> Guided

(a) Give **two** reasons why using cloud computing will help Tony in his work. | (2 marks)

One way that cloud computing could benefit Tony is that it is available anywhere where there

is an internet connection, so he can ..............................................................................................

..........................................................................................................................................................

Another way that cloud computing could benefit Tony is ...........................................................

..........................................................................................................................................................

............................................................................

> Make sure your answer is specific to the scenario.

Tony realises there are risks to relying on cloud computing.

(b) Describe **two** disadvantages of cloud computing for Tony. | (2 marks)

..........................................................................................................................................................

..........................................................................................................................................................

..........................................................................................................................................................

..........................................................................................................................................................

# Ubiquitous computing

**1**  Which of these is a type of chip often used in ubiquitous computing?   **(1 mark)**

**A** ☐ RFID

**B** ☐ USB

**C** ☐ IP

**D** ☐ TCP

**2**  Describe 'ubiquitous computing'.   **(2 marks)**

..................................................................................................................................................

..................................................................................................................................................

⟩ **Guided** ⟩ **3**  Give **one** example of ubiquitous computing for each of the areas in the table.   **(2 marks)**

| Household appliances | Ubiquitous computing can be processors embedded in washing machines to control how the clothes are washed. |
|---|---|
| Animals or people | |
| Shopping | |

**4**  Write a sales pitch to a taxi company explaining the advantages of fitting tracking devices to their fleet of taxis.   **(4 marks)**

..................................................................................................................................................

..................................................................................................................................................

..................................................................................................................................................

..................................................................................................................................................

> Think about how a tracking device would help a taxi company.

# The internet – hardware

**1** Define the term 'the internet'. **(1 mark)**

......................................................................................................................................................

**2** Label the **three** devices in this network. **(3 marks)**

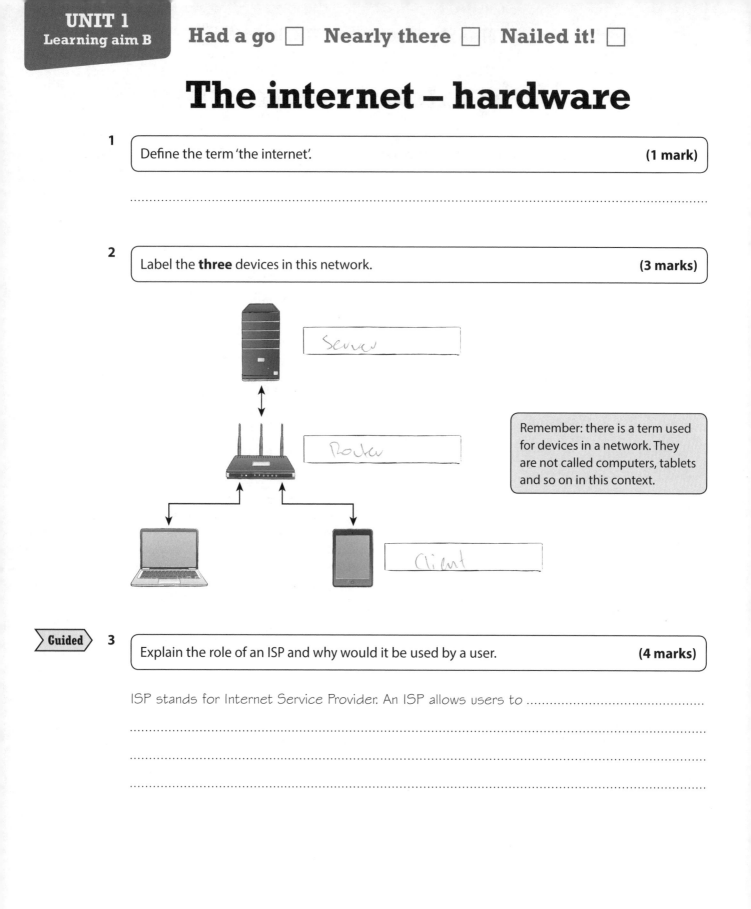

Server

Router

Remember: there is a term used for devices in a network. They are not called computers, tablets and so on in this context.

Client

⟩ **Guided** ⟩ **3** Explain the role of an ISP and why would it be used by a user. **(4 marks)**

ISP stands for Internet Service Provider. An ISP allows users to .............................................

......................................................................................................................................................

......................................................................................................................................................

......................................................................................................................................................

# The internet – network diagrams

> **Guided**

**1** Identify what an ISP might have several of to allow users good access to the internet.

**(1 mark)**

PO .........          (Point of ................................)

**2** Complete the labels in this network.

**(2 marks)**

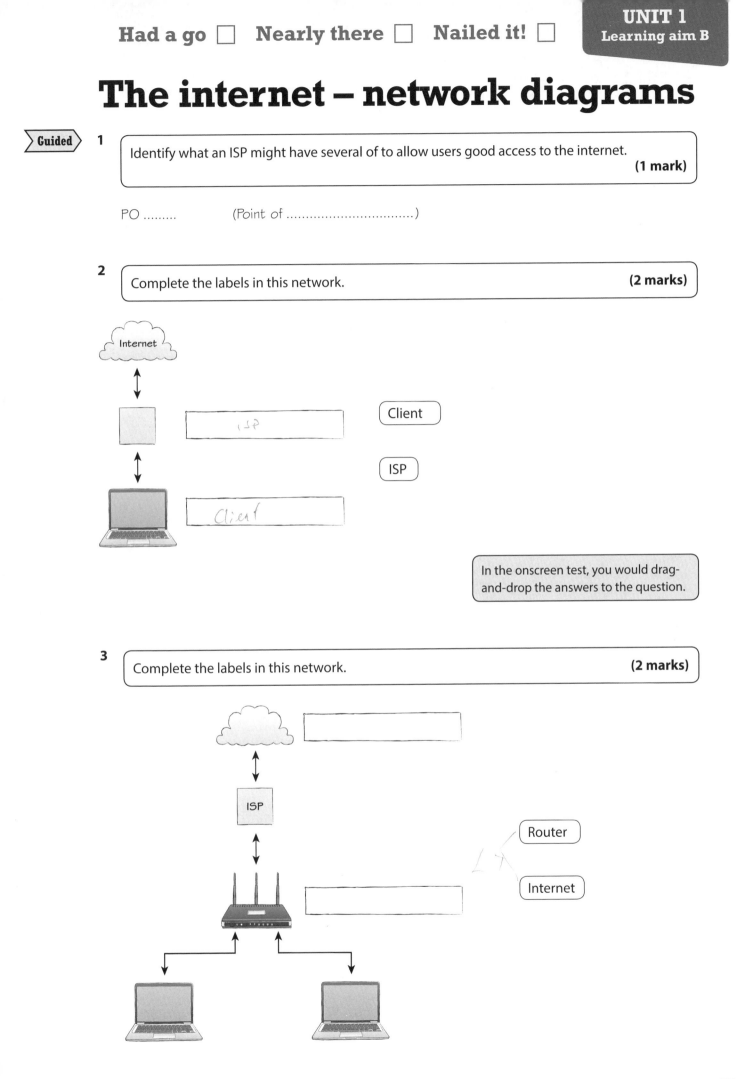

Internet

ISP

Client

ISP

Client

In the onscreen test, you would drag-and-drop the answers to the question.

**3** Complete the labels in this network.

**(2 marks)**

ISP

Router

Internet

# Connection methods

1   Complete the table below identifying and describing **two** types of internet connection.
    Some information has been given for you.                                    **(2 marks)**

| Internet connection method | Description |
|---|---|
| Wireless | Connection without wires |
| Dial-up | |

2   Explain how high bandwidth would allow a website to load quickly on a user's computer.
    **(2 marks)**

.................................................................................................................................

.................................................................................................................................

3   Abi is trying to decide which type of internet connection she should use at home.

> Guided

**(a)** Describe **one** advantage and **one** disadvantage of a dial-up connection.     **(4 marks)**

An advantage of dial-up is that it uses existing telephone lines so it would be good if Abi

was based where other services were not available. However, older ........................................

.................................................................................................................................

.................................................................................................................................

.................................................................................................................................

**(b)** Describe **one** advantage and **one** disadvantage of a wireless connection.     **(4 marks)**

.................................................................................................................................

.................................................................................................................................

.................................................................................................................................

# The internet – protocols

**1**   Explain the role of a protocol.     **(2 marks)**

...................................................................................................................................................................

...................................................................................................................................................................

**2**   **(a)** Which **two** protocols work together to transfer data across the internet?     **(2 marks)**

A ☐   FTP

B ☐   IP

C ☐   HTTP

D ☐   TCP

   **(b)** Which networking method is used by all of the four protocols listed in question **2(a)**?
    **(1 mark)**

A ☐   Packet switching

B ☐   Circuit switching

C ☐   Protocol switching

D ☐   Network switching

**Guided**   **3**   Complete the table to describe what each protocol does.     **(4 marks)**

| Protocol | Main purpose |
|---|---|
| TCP | TCP takes data from the user's application and passes it to IP for transfer across the internet. It organises data into packets. |
| IP | |
| FTP | |

# World Wide Web

**1**

> Select the appropriate descriptions for each term from the box below. **(2 marks)**

Web browsers ......................................................................................................................

Web servers .......................................................................................................................

| Display web pages |
| Store web pages |

> In the onscreen test, you would drag and drop the answers into the correct place.

**Guided**  **2**

> Describe what happens when a user requests a web page. **(3 marks)**

A user requests a web page using a web address/URL. A copy of the web page is then .........

..........................................................................................................................................

..........................................................................................................................................

..........................................................................................................................................

**3**

> **(a)** State what functionality connects web pages together. **(1 mark)**

..........................................................................................................................................

> **(b)** Explain how your answer to question **3a** works from a user's perspective. **(2 marks)**

..........................................................................................................................................

..........................................................................................................................................

# HTML

**1**  Which of the following is HTML?  **(1 mark)**

**A** ☐  A protocol

**B** ☐  An application

**C** ☐  A URL

**D** ☐ ✓  A language

**2**  Complete the HTML to create a hyperlink to www.candles.com with the phrase "Buy candles here" displayed on screen.  **(2 marks)**

........................  www.candles.com  ........................

**Guided**  **3**  Using the HTML elements below, complete the table. One example answer has been provided for you.  **(3 marks)**

| | |
|---|---|
| <b> | bold |
| <i> | italic |
| <p> | paragraph |
| <img=> | image |
| <a href> | hyperlink |
| <li> | list |
| <ul> | bullet |

Note: These HTML elements are to help you but are not part of the question

| HTML | Displayed on web page |
|---|---|
| <i>Sunflower</i> | |
| | **Daffodil** |
| <li><br><ul>Daisy</ul><br><ul>Dandelion</ul><br><ul>Bluebell</ul><br></li> | list bullet *clear both* |

**17**

# URLs

**1**

**(a)** What does URL stand for?                                                    **(1 mark)**

Uniform Resource Locator

**(b)** What is a URL?                                                              **(1 mark)**

ULR – is the link that you typing into browser.

**2**

What does HTTP stand for?                                                          **(1 mark)**

**Guided** **3**

Label the **three** parts of this URL.                                              **(3 marks)**

In the onscreen test, you would drag-and-drop the answers to the question.

## http://www.lancashiremuseums.co.uk/visit/january/

| Protocol | Domain Name | Path |

protocol

domain name

path

**4**

Outline the difference between the two following links.                            **(2 marks)**

http://www.lancashiremuseums.co.uk/visit/map.pdf

ftp://www.lancashiremuseums.co.uk/visit/map.pdf

Use diff. protocol

# Search engines

**1**

(a) Which of these is **not** a term for the software used by search engines? **(1 mark)**

A ☐ Spiders

B ☐ Bugs

C ☐ Crawlers

D ☐ Bots

(b) Identify what search engine software is looking for on the internet. **(1 mark)**

........................................................................................................................................

(c) When they have found what they are looking for, where are the results of this search stored? **(1 mark)**

........................................................................................................................................

(d) How often does this storing process happen? **(1 mark)**

A ☐ All the time

B ☐ Every now and again

C ☐ Once an hour

> **Guided** **2**

Complete the table by putting the search results in the order they would be displayed. **(2 marks)**

In the onscreen test these would be drag-and-drop.

| |
|---|
| |
| |
| Less popular result |

| |
|---|
| Less popular result |
| Most popular result |
| Sponsored link |

2 marks are given because if you get two correct then the third must be correct.

**3**

Complete the table by putting the actions of a search engine in the order that they will be completed. **(2 marks)**

| |
|---|
| |
| |
| |

| |
|---|
| Results are displayed |
| User enters key words |
| The database is searched |

2 marks are given because if you get two correct then the third must be correct.

# Email – purposes and uses

**1**

What **two** methods can be used to send emails to multiple recipients? **(2 marks)**

A ☐ CB   B ☐ BCB   C ☒ BCC   D ☒ CC   E ☐ CE

**2**

What are the **three** actions a user can take to send an email they have received to another user? **(3 marks)**

..................................................................................................................................

..................................................................................................................................

..................................................................................................................................

**3**

Label the different parts of this email. **(3 marks)**

File Attachme

Untitled - Message (HTML)

File   Edit   View   Insert   Format   Tools   Actions   Help

Send   Options...   Arial   10   A B I

To...

Cc...

Subject:

Subject

Each of these labels should be appropriate key terms.

**Guided**   **4**   David is a news journalist working for a UK TV company. He uses email to communicate with the news desk in London.

State **two** advantages and **two** disadvantages of this. **(8 marks)**

One of the advantages of email for David is that he can send attachments with his emails. This means ...................................................................................................................

..................................................................................................................................

..................................................................................................................................

..................................................................................................................................

One disadvantage is that there is a security risk. If David has a good story then he would not want a hacker to

..................................................................

..................................................................

..................................................................

Consider how you will structure your answer, based on the 8 marks available. Think about writing a plan before you start, making sure you include both advantages and disadvantages.

# Email – protocols

**1**   Identify the type of email which would be most likely to use the IMAP protocol.   **(1 mark)**

.................................................................................................................................................

**2**   Connect up the protocol to its action.   **(2 marks)**

Forward

SMTP    Pull

Push

POP3    Back

Reverse

> There are two marks available so you only need to connect each protocol to one answer.

**3**   Usma is a student at Sheffield University studying to be a teacher. She is going on work placement in a school two days a week. She is considering setting up a web mail account as she will be travelling between the placement, university and home.

Discuss the advantages and disadvantages of this.   **(4 marks)**

.................................................................................................................................................

.................................................................................................................................................

.................................................................................................................................................

.................................................................................................................................................

.................................................................................................................................................

# Data exchange – packet switching

**1** Which of the following is **not** part of a data packet? **(1 mark)**

A ☐ Destination address

B ☐ Payload

C ☐ Route instructions

D ☐ Error control bits

**2** Explain why packet switching is an efficient method of sending data through the internet. **(2 marks)**

......................................................................................................................................

......................................................................................................................................

**3** Explain **one** drawback to packet switching. **(2 marks)**

......................................................................................................................................

......................................................................................................................................

> **Guided** **4** Complete the table describing parts of a data packet. **(5 marks)**

| Data packet parts | Description |
|---|---|
| Packet identification | Gives each packet an ID so it can be identified when it is to be put back together |
| | Location of the recipient's computer |
| Source address | |
| Payload | The data being carried by the packet |
| Error control bits | |

Make sure you complete all parts of the table in order to gain all 5 marks.

# Data exchange – transmission modes

**1**

> Which of the following is **not** a transmission mode?  **(1 mark)**

**A** ☐ Simplex

**B** ☐ Half-simplex

**C** ☑ Half-duplex

**D** ☐ Full-duplex

**2**  USB is a type of serial device.

> **Guided**

> **(a)** Explain what is meant by a serial transmission mode.  **(2 marks)**

A serial transmission mode sends bits of data one at a time over ...........................................

.......................................................................................................................................

> **(b)** Explain why parallel is a faster transmission mode than serial.  **(2 marks)**

.......................................................................................................................................

.......................................................................................................................................

**3**

> Complete the table by suggesting suitable devices for each transmission mode and describing the direction of data transfer.  **(6 marks)**

| Transmission mode | Direction | Example device |
|---|---|---|
| Full-duplex |  |  |
| Half-duplex |  |  |
| Simplex |  |  |

> Think about all the information you have to give here in order to gain all 6 marks.

# Wired transmission methods

**1** In UTP and STP cables, what is the main reason that the copper wires are twisted? **(1 mark)**

A ☐ To make the cables smaller    B ☐ To keep the price of the cables cheap

C ☐ To cancel out interference    D ☐ To ensure the cables are flexible

**2** Outline the difference between UTP and STP cables. **(2 marks)**

......................................................................................................................................

......................................................................................................................................

**3** Select **one** correct limitation for each type of transmission method. **(3 marks)**

UTP          Most expensive to install          Draw a line between the term and the correct explanation.

Coaxial      Slowest and lowest capacity

Fibre optic  Susceptible to noise

Try using elimination to work out the correct answers.

**Guided** **4** A large office block has different businesses on each floor. As part of their rent they have access to the building's network. The office block uses fibre optic as a backbone and STP for each individual computer to connect to the backbone.

Discuss why these are appropriate types of transmission methods. **(8 marks)**

Fibre optic is an appropriate type to use for the backbone because it is a fast method of

transmission for the backbone of the office. It has a high data capacity because ....................

......................................................................................................................................

......................................................................................................................................

STP is an appropriate type to connect each computer to the backbone because it is

cheaper than ....................................................................................................................

......................................................................................................................................

......................................................................................................................................

......................................................................................................................................

......................................................................................................................................

# Wireless transmission methods

**1**

> Which of the following type of waves are used in Bluetooth technology? **(1 mark)**

**A** ☐ Infrared waves

**B** ☐ Ultraviolet waves

**C** ☐ Alpha waves

**D** ☒ Microwaves

> Guided **2**

> Complete the table using the data from the box below. **(3 marks)**

> In the onscreen test, you would drag-and-drop the answers into the table.

| Wireless transmission methods | Approximate data transfer rate | Approximate range |
|---|---|---|
| Infrared | 4 Mbps | |
| Microwave | | |
| Satellite | | 20,000 km |

| | | |
|---|---|---|
| 100 Gbps | 100 m | 4 Mbps |
| 20,000 km | 100 Mbps | 10 m |

> You should be able to work out which are the most appropriate sizes with what you know about these transmission methods.

> The sizes are measured in distance (metres or kilometres) and data/speed (Mb or Gb per second) – the same types of measurement will be in each column.

**3** A café offers free wireless internet access to its customers.

> Discuss the benefits and limitations for the café offering this service. **(4 marks)**

..............................................................................................................................

..............................................................................................................................

..............................................................................................................................

..............................................................................................................................

# Client-side processing

**1** Identify where the processing occurs in client-side processing. **(1 mark)**

............................................................................................................................

**Guided** **2** Complete these sentences about client-side processing, using the words from the box below. **(3 marks)**

| code/script | interactivity | downloaded |

> In the onscreen test, these would be drop-down boxes.

Client-side processing can produce interactivity on a web page.

When a web page is requested, a copy is ......................................... onto the client's computer.

This is created on the web page using ...................................... .

> If you are having trouble with questions like this then start with the answers you **do** know.

**3** An online clothes retailer is updating their website to promote and sell their clothes. They are considering using client-side processing.

Using examples, discuss **two** advantages and **two** disadvantages of client-side processing. **(8 marks)**

............................................................................................................................

............................................................................................................................

............................................................................................................................

............................................................................................................................

............................................................................................................................

............................................................................................................................

............................................................................................................................

............................................................................................................................

# Server-side processing

**1**

Identify where the processing occurs in server-side processing.　**(1 mark)**

...................................................................................................................................

**2**

**(a)** Describe the term 'browser-specific' with relation to web scripts.　**(2 marks)**

...................................................................................................................................

...................................................................................................................................

**(b)** Explain why client-side scripting is browser-specific and server-side scripting is not browser-specific.　**(2 marks)**

...................................................................................................................................

...................................................................................................................................

**Guided**　**3**　An online clothes retailer is updating their website to promote and sell their clothes. They are planning to use a server-side processed online form to allow users to sign up for an account.

Using examples, discuss the advantages of server-side processing.　**(4 marks)**

An advantage of server-side processing for the retailer is efficiency because ........................

...................................................................................................................................

...................................................................................................................................

Another advantage of server-side processing is that it is browser ...................................

...................................................................................................................................

...................................................................................................................................

# Threats to data

**1** Computer viruses are often described as malicious software.

> Explain what is meant by the term 'computer viruses'.    **(2 marks)**

................................................................................................................................................

................................................................................................................................................

**Guided**   **2**

> Define the term 'phishing'.    **(1 mark)**

*Phishing means an email or website pretending to be* ..................................................................

................................................................................................................................................

> Try to learn the definitions of as many key terms as you can.

**3** Accidental damage can be caused by natural disasters such as flood, fires or hurricanes.

> **(a)** Identify a method of accidental damage which is not a natural disaster.    **(1 mark)**

................................................................................................................................................

> **(b)** Explain the difference between accidental damage and opportunist threat.    **(2 marks)**

................................................................................................................................................

................................................................................................................................................

................................................................................................................................................

................................................................................................................................................

# Protection of data

1
> This password has **four** aspects which make it a strong password. Mark on the password what these aspects are. One has been done for you. **(3 marks)**

| More than eight characters | ———— Wd?8plane |

2
> This is the computer security tick list for an office. Complete the list with **two** more physical security methods. **(2 marks)**

Security checklist

1. Lock doors

2.

3.

> Guided  3
> Complete the table below by identifying the threats and appropriate methods of prevention. **(6 marks)**

| Threat | Prevention method | Explanation of prevention method |
|---|---|---|
| Virus | | Monitors files and deletes viruses or quarantines infected files |
| | Firewall | |
| | Encryption | |
| New, untrained members of staff | Levels of access | Restricts access to only the data they need to view or edit |

4
> Explain why backup and recovery are important in case a threat is not prevented. **(4 marks)**

...................................................................................................

...................................................................................................

...................................................................................  | You need to explain both aspects of the question to get 4 marks here. |

...................................................................................

# Legislation

1    Which UK law protects the customer's data which is stored by businesses?    **(1 mark)**

.................................................................................................................................

**Guided**   2    The Computer Misuse Act was passed in the UK to punish (and therefore prevent against) which **two** types of threats?    **(2 marks)**

**1** Hackers

**2** .........................................................................................................................

3    Geoff subscribes and pays a fee to a music website from where he downloads music legally. Katherine downloads music illegally.

Discuss this situation, including UK copyright law.    **(8 marks)**

.................................................................................................................................

.................................................................................................................................

.................................................................................................................................

.................................................................................................................................

.................................................................................................................................

.................................................................................................................................

.................................................................................................................................

.................................................................................................................................

.................................................................................................................................

.................................................................................................................................

.................................................................................................................

.................................................................................................................

.................................................................................................................

> Think carefully about all the information you need to provide in order to get the full 8 marks available.

# Exam skills 1

**Guided**   1

Which **two** of these cables use copper to transfer data?   **(2 marks)**

A ☒ UTP

B ☐ Fibre optic

C ☐ Coaxial

D ☐ Microwaves

E ☐ Bluetooth

> Make sure you read the question carefully – this asks for **two** answers.

2   In a solicitor's office, different levels of access are given to employees depending on their job role.

Match the appropriate level of access to the users.   **(3 marks)**

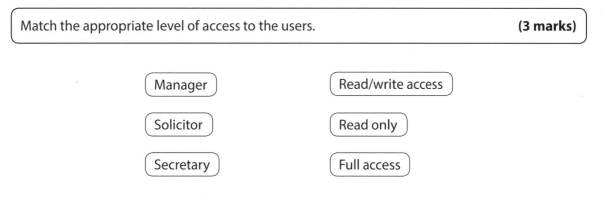

Manager     Read/write access

Solicitor     Read only

Secretary     Full access

3   Below is a packet of data being sent through a network.

Complete the packet by placing the sections from below in the correct order.   **(3 marks)**

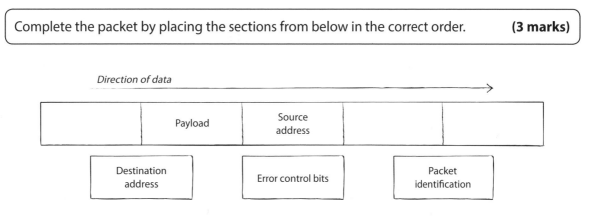

*Direction of data*

| | Payload | Source address | | |

Destination address    Error control bits    Packet identification

# Exam skills 2

**1** Which **one** of these internet hardware items is directly used by the user? **(1 mark)**

A ☐ Server

B ☐ Client

C ☐ Router

D ☐ Backbone

Guided **2** Select **two** benefits of email from the list below. **(2 marks)**

| |
|---|
| Employees may spend time sending personal emails at work |
| Employees can send messages to multiple people at the same time |
| Employees may be sent spam |
| Employees may receive phishing emails |
| Employees can access contacts in their address book |

In the onscreen test, you would be able to click on the text and the box would highlight (as shown) to show you have chosen it.

**3** Drag the labels to identify different elements of the screenshot of an instant messenger program.

**(3 marks)**

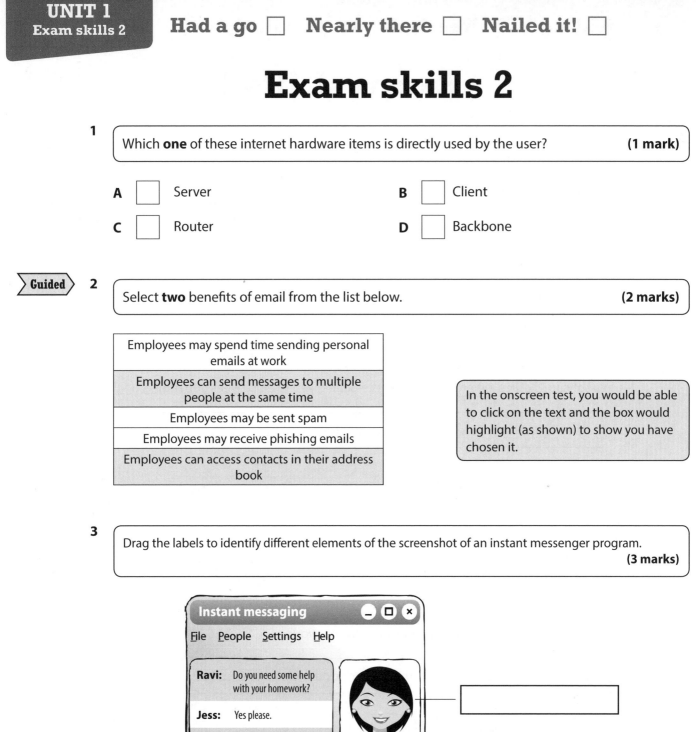

| Username | Example of bad netiquette | Avatar |
|---|---|---|

# Exam skills 3

 **1**

Describe the difference between serial and parallel communication.    **(2 marks)**

| Serial | Sends one bit at a time |
|---|---|
| Parallel | |

**2**

Describe **two** threats to the security of data on the internet.    **(4 marks)**

.................................................................................................................................

.................................................................................................................................

.................................................................................................................................

.................................................................................................................................

> You have been asked for **two** threats and the question is worth four marks – for each one give an expansion such as 'because…'.

**3**

Discuss the benefits and drawbacks of cloud computing.    **(8 marks)**

.................................................................................................................................

.................................................................................................................................

.................................................................................................................................

.................................................................................................................................

.................................................................................................................................

.................................................................................................................................

.................................................................................................................................

.................................................................................................................................

.................................................................................................................................

.................................................................................................................................

.................................................................................................................................

.................................................................................................................................

> Think about how you structure your answer. Plan it on paper first. Think about discussing **two** positives and **two** negatives – then expand on those four points.

# Technology systems

**1**

Which **one** of these sectors might use CAD/CAM? **(1 mark)**

A ☐ Health

B ☐ Finance

C ☐ Manufacturing

D ☐ Retail

**2**

Explain **one** way that the health sector uses technology to care for patients. **(2 marks)**

.................................................................................................................................

.................................................................................................................................

**3**

State **one** type of PoS technology. **(1 mark)**

.................................................................................................................................

**4**

Describe **one** benefit of this for customers. **(1 mark)**

.................................................................................................................................

**5**

Describe **two** benefits of this for sellers. **(2 marks)**

.................................................................................................................................

.................................................................................................................................

.................................................................................................................................

.................................................................................................................................

# Issues in technology systems

**1**

> Which **one** of these terms means 'using resources to meet current needs without taking away resources for the future'? **(1 mark)**

**A** ☐ Sustainability

**B** ☐ Carbon footprint

**C** ☐ Greenhouse effect

**D** ☐ Renewable energy

**2** Malware is a threat to computer security.

> Identify **two** examples of malware. **(2 marks)**

.......................................................................................................................................

.......................................................................................................................................

**3** All computer systems are at risk of attacks from unauthorised sources.

> Describe **two** ways in which a user can use software to protect their system from these types of attacks. **(2 marks)**

.......................................................................................................................................

.......................................................................................................................................

.......................................................................................................................................

.......................................................................................................................................

**Guided**  **4**

> Explain how the production of a smartphone can be damaging to the environment. **(2 marks)**

Smartphones are made from metals, such as tin, which need to be mined from the ground.

This can damage the environment because ............................................................................

.......................................................................................................................................

.......................................................................................................................................

# Developing technology systems

**1**    Which **one** of these is **not** a typical reason for developing technology?    **(1 mark)**

A ☐ Reduced costs

B ☐ Competitive advantage

C ☐ Improved performance

> Read the question carefully –
> have you spotted the 'not'?

D ☐ Reduced revenue

**2**    Match the reasons for developing technology with the example reasons.    **(3 marks)**

| Improved performance | | Improving delivery routes which requires less petrol in the vehicles |
| Competitive advantage | | Improving user interface of software to make it easier to use |
| Reduced costs | | Improving the product so it has more functionality for the same price |

**Guided**   **3**    A washing machine manufacturer is considering developing its production line technology to use more robots.

> Explain **one** reason for doing this and **one** positive and **one** negative potential impact on the company.    **(5 marks)**

The manufacturer is developing its technology because ...............................................................................

................................................................................................................................................................................

................................................................................................................................................................................

A positive impact on the company is .......................................................................................................

................................................................................................................................................................................

................................................................................................................................................................................

A negative impact on the company is .......................................................................................................

................................................................................................................................................................................

................................................................................................................................................................................

# Hardware devices

**1**  Peter needs a portable device to use for web browsing, watching movies and using his calendar.

> Choose a suitable device.  **(1 mark)**

**A** ☐  Server          **B** ☐  Tablet          **C** ☐  PC          **D** ☐  Games console

**2**  A microwave, washing machine and cooker are all programmable digital devices.

> What **one** component will they all have which allows them to be programmed and carry out instructions?  **(1 mark)**

.......................................................................................................................................................

**3**  Samantha uses a paper diary at work which she carries with her to meetings and uses all of the time.

> Describe **two** reasons why she could use a tablet instead.  **(2 marks)**

.......................................................................................................................................................

.......................................................................................................................................................

⟩ **Guided** ⟩  **4**  Mohammed is buying a new device to play a recently released video game. He is choosing between a PC, a laptop and a games console. These three devices are within his budget and compatible with the game he wants to play.  **(6 marks)**

> **(a)** The PC has a graphics expansion card installed and has the highest graphics capabilities with dedicated GPU. Explain how this works and the effect it will have on the game.  **(2 marks)**

.......................................................................................................................................................

.......................................................................................................................................................

> **(b)** The laptop is portable. Identify **one** advantage of this.  **(1 mark)**

.......................................................................................................................................................

> **(c)** The game needs an internet connection for it to run. Identify **one** disadvantage of choosing the laptop.  **(1 mark)**

.......................................................................................................................................................

> **(d)** The games console uses cloud storage. Explain **two** benefits of this.  **(2 marks)**

.......................................................................................................................................................

.......................................................................................................................................................

# Input and output

**1**  Complete this diagram, which represents a technology device. Choose the correct **two** words from the word box.  **(2 marks)**

⟹   | Process |   ⟹

| decision | output | storage | peripheral | input |

**2**  Which of these is an output device?  **(1 mark)**

**A** ☐  Microphone      **B** ☐  Scanner      **C** ☐  Digital camera      **D** ☐  Projector

**3**  A touch screen, such as on a smartphone, can be used for both input and output. Explain why this is.  **(4 marks)**

...................................................................................................................................................

...................................................................................................................................................

...................................................................................................................................................

...................................................................................................................................................

**Guided**  **4**  Match the input and output devices to the technology systems.  **(4 marks)**

| Actuator | | Video conferencing |
| Microphone | | Games console |
| Sensor | | Radio-controlled car |
| Force feedback | | Car wash |

# Storage

**1** **(a)** Identify this storage device.    **(1 mark)**

A ☐ HDD                B ☐ SSD

C ☐ Optical drive       D ☐ Floppy disk drive

> Guided

**(b)** Explain how an HDD storage device works.    **(4 marks)**

The magnetic disk ...............................................................................................................

....................................................................................................................................

The read/write head ............................................................................................................

....................................................................................................................................

**2** Dinah wants to buy an external storage device. She is considering whether to buy an HDD or an SSD.

Compare the drives and list **two** benefits of a hard disk drive and **two** benefits of a solid state drive by completing the table below.    **(4 marks)**

| Hard disk drive | Solid state drive |
| --- | --- |
| Benefit 1: | Benefit 1: |
| Benefit 2: | Benefit 2: |

**3** Match the type of storage to the description.    **(1 mark)**

| | | |
| --- | --- | --- |
| CD | | A disk that is blank but can be written to once by the user but then the data is fixed. |
| CD-R | | A blank CD that can be written to several times by the user. |
| CD-RW | | A disk that has already been written to and can't be changed. |

# Automated systems

1   Robots are used to explore space and other planets, such as the Mars Rover or Jade Rabbit on the Moon.

> Explain **one** reason why robots are used instead of humans.  **(2 marks)**

.......................................................................................................................................................

.......................................................................................................................................................

2   
> Explain how **one** input and **one** output device operate on this automated system.  **(2 marks)**

.......................................................................................................................................................

.......................................................................................................................................................

.......................................................................................................................................................

.......................................................................................................................................................

.......................................................................................................................................................

.......................................................................................................................................................

> Think about the inputs – how does the production line know where the car is positioned?

> Think about the outputs – what does the work on the production line?

# Devices to capture data

**1**   Which **one** of these devices would be used for reading students' multiple choice exam papers?
**(1 mark)**

A ☐   RFID         B ☐   OMR

C ☐   OCR         D ☐   Magnetic strip reader

**2**   Klara is researching her family history and has found an old newspaper article. She wants to keep digital records of all of the information she finds.

What automated device can she use to scan the document into text?      **(1 mark)**

..............................................................................................................................................

**3**   Indus is a company that sells DVDs, books and video games online. They have warehouses where the products are stored in huge quantities. They track the products using RFID chips embedded into the labels of each item's packaging. When they pass through scanners the items are logged, either going into the warehouse to be stored or out to be delivered to the customer.

Explain **two** advantages and **two** disadvantages of using RFID chips for this warehouse system.      **(8 marks)**

..............................................................................................................................................

..............................................................................................................................................

..............................................................................................................................................

..............................................................................................................................................

..............................................................................................................................................

..............................................................................................................................................

..............................................................................................................................................

..............................................................................................................................................

# Types and uses of networks

**1**   What type of network is the internet?    **(1 mark)**

**A** ☐ LAN     **B** ☐ WAN     **C** ☐ PAN     **D** ☐ MAN

**2**   Describe how a mobile device could connect to a local area network.    **(1 mark)**

...............................................................................................................

**3**   Give **four** examples of data that can be synchronised between a smartphone and PC.

   **(2 marks)**

| Example 1 | |
|---|---|
| Example 2 | |
| Example 3 | |
| Example 4 | |

**4**   Match the networks with the explanations.    **(3 marks)**

| | |
|---|---|
| PAN | A network that spans several countries |
| WAN | A network that is in one office or building |
| LAN | A network that includes a few devices close to each other, e.g. devices in a personal space |

# Benefits of networks

1    Which **one** of these is not a strength of networking?    **(1 mark)**

A    ☐    Communication

B    ☐    Security

C    ☐    Sharing resources

D    ☐    Entertainment

2    Vimala is in Malaysia and Jonathan is in the UK.

Explain, using **two** examples, how they could use a network to communicate.    **(4 marks)**

........................................................................................................................................................

........................................................................................................................................................

........................................................................................................................................................

........................................................................................................................................................

**Guided**    3    Complete this mind map of the benefits of using a network.    **(4 marks)**

Improves efficiency

Benefits of networking

# Methods of transferring data

1
> What material is used in fibre optic cables to transfer light as data?  **(1 mark)**

A ☐ Copper wire

B ☐ Glass

C ☐ Aluminium

D ☐ Rubber

2
> Match the type of physical network connections to the uses.  **(3 marks)**

| | |
|---|---|
| UTP | Connecting to a cable television network |
| Fibre optic | Connecting PCs to routers in a network |
| Coaxial | Backbone of a network, connecting routers to servers |

⟩ **Guided** ⟩  3
> Describe the difference between physical (or wired) and wireless networking and give examples of where each might be more appropriate.  **(5 marks)**

A physical network is where each device is connected through a wire. An example is ...............

.................................................................................................................................................

.................................................................................................................................................

.................................................................................................................................................

.................................................................................................................................................

# Main components of a computer

1

> Which of these **two** components need to be cooled when running?   **(2 marks)**

A ☐ RAM

B ☐ HDD

C ☐ CPU

D ☐ PSU

E ☐ ROM

2

> **(a)** State the main role of the CPU.   **(1 mark)**

.......................................................................................................................................................................

> **(b)** State the main role of a Hard Disk Drive.   **(1 mark)**

.......................................................................................................................................................................

> Guided   3

> Explain, using examples, what expansion cards are and what role they play in a PC.   **(4 marks)**

Expansion cards can be for sound or ...................................................................................................................

.......................................................................................................................................................................

.......................................................................................................................................................................

.......................................................................................................................................................................

.......................................................................................................................................................................

# Processing digital data 1

**1**

Which **one** of these is processed by the CPU? **(1 mark)**

**A** ☐ Denary

**B** ☐ Hexadecimal

**C** ☐ Instructions

**D** ☐ RAM

**2**

**(a)** Complete this diagram representing how the CPU and other components interact inside a PC by choosing the correct term. **(3 marks)**

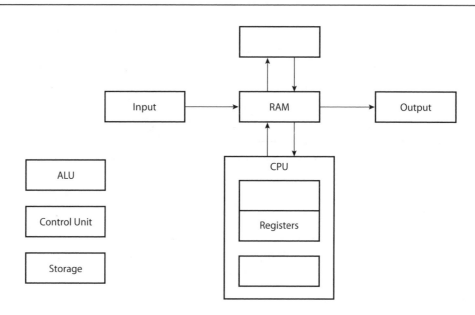

**(b)** State what the ALU/Registers and control unit do. **(2 marks)**

..........................................................................................................................................

..........................................................................................................................................

..........................................................................................................................................

..........................................................................................................................................

..........................................................................................................................................

..........................................................................................................................................

# Processing digital data 2

1   How much data can be processed in one clock cycle?   **(1 mark)**

   A ☐   One bit

   B ☐   One byte

   C ☐   One word

   D ☐   One character

2   What is the purpose of cache memory and where might it be used?   **(2 marks)**

   ....................................................................................................................................................................

   ....................................................................................................................................................................

3   **(a)** Describe the role of a data bus.   **(2 marks)**

   ....................................................................................................................................................................

   ....................................................................................................................................................................

   **(b)** What happens if you increase the size of the data bus?   **(1 mark)**

   ....................................................................................................................................................................

Guided   4   A CPU has the following specification: quad core 2GHz. What does this mean?   **(4 marks)**

   Quad core means that the processor has four cores, which .............................................................

   ....................................................................................................................................................................

   ....................................................................................................................................................................

   2 GHz is the measurement of the clock cycles. For each clock cycle .............................................

   ....................................................................................................................................................................

   ....................................................................................................................................................................

# Memory and storage

1

**(a)** Which **one** of these statements about ROM is true? **(1 mark)**

A ☐ Temporary and a type of memory

B ☐ Temporary and a type of storage

C ☐ Permanent and a type of memory

D ☐ Permanent and a type of storage

**(b)** Describe the purpose of the ROM chip on a PC's motherboard. **(2 marks)**

.......................................................................................................................................................

.......................................................................................................................................................

2

**(a)** RAM is temporary memory. What does temporary mean in this context? **(1 mark)**

.......................................................................................................................................................

**(b)** What is the purpose of RAM? **(1 mark)**

.......................................................................................................................................................

3

**(a)** Complete these names of types of RAM. **(2 marks)**

| DRAM | D_____ Random Access Memory |
|------|----------------------------------------|
| SRAM | S_____ Random Access Memory |

**(b)** Identify the type of RAM for each device. **(1 mark)**

| Device | Type of RAM |
|--------|-------------|
| | |
| | |

# Mobile devices

**1**   Where would the processing happen in a typical smartphone?     **(1 mark)**

**A** ☐ CPU

**B** ☐ SoC

**C** ☐ GPU

**D** ☐ RAM

> Consider the components inside a smartphone – are they different from a PC or laptop?

**Guided**   **2**   **(a)** What factors are important for developing a mobile device?     **(5 marks)**

| W | S | B | Interface | F |
|---|---|---|---|---|
|   |   |   |   |   |

> The initial letters of the missing answers are given to help you.

**(b)** Describe **two** reasons why mobile device manufacturers should consider these factors when designing new devices.     **(2 marks)**

.......................................................................................................................................

.......................................................................................................................................

.......................................................................................................................................

.......................................................................................................................................

# Analogue and digital data

1 | Describe the difference between analogue and digital data. **(2 marks)**

....................................................................................................................................

....................................................................................................................................

2 | Explain how analogue data is turned into digital data. **(2 marks)**

....................................................................................................................................

....................................................................................................................................

....................................................................................................................................

....................................................................................... | Sampling is involved.

....................................................................................................................................

**Guided** 3 | Complete the labels in this diagram to show how data is converted from digital to analogue to transfer voice data over the internet. **(2 marks)**

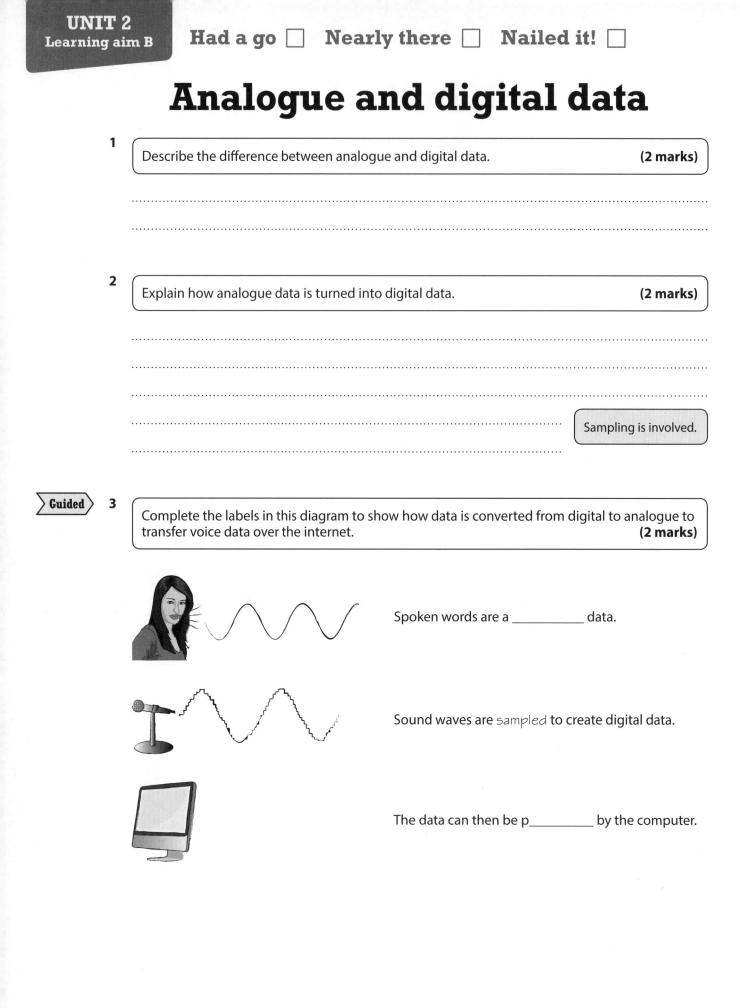

Spoken words are a _____ data.

Sound waves are *sampled* to create digital data.

The data can then be p_____ by the computer.

# Converting denary to binary

**1**

> Convert 7 to binary (base 2) and show your workings.    **(2 marks)**

**2**

> Convert these numbers to binary (base 2).    **(6 marks)**

| (a) | 0 | |
|-----|---|---|
| (b) | 1 | |
| (c) | 2 | |
| (d) | 3 | |
| (e) | 4 | |
| (f) | 5 | |

# Converting binary to denary

**1**    Convert 00001010 to denary (base 10) and show your workings.    **(2 marks)**

**2**    Convert these numbers to denary (base 10).    **(5 marks)**

| (a) | 10001100 | |
| --- | --- | --- |
| (b) | 10101111 | |
| (c) | 11011101 | |
| (d) | 01101110 | |
| (e) | 00010001 | |

**Guided**    **3**    Windows 7 is released in 32-bit and 64-bit. This refers to the word length of the processor. Explain how the difference in word length affects the two versions.    **(8 marks)**

A word is a fixed number of bits e.g. 32-bit and 64-bit. A word is the amount of data which

can be processed in ................................................................................................................................

..........................................................................................................................................................

..........................................................................................................................................................

..........................................................................................................................................................

..........................................................................................................................................................

..........................................................................................................................................................

..........................................................................................................................................................

# Software

**1**

> What is software? **(1 mark)**

....................................................................................................................................................

**2**

> What type of software is Microsoft® Office? Choose one option. **(1 mark)**

**A** ☐ Custom-made

**B** ☐ Bespoke

**C** ☐ Off-the-shelf

**D** ☐ Shareware

**Guided**  **3**  A customer services department is considering buying new software. The staff are comparing off-the-shelf and custom-made.

> Discuss **one** advantage and **one** disadvantage of **each** type. **(8 marks)**

One advantage of off-the-shelf software is ...................................................................................

....................................................................................................................................................

....................................................................................................................................................

One disadvantage of off-the-shelf software is ...........................................................................

....................................................................................................................................................

....................................................................................................................................................

One advantage of custom-made software is ..............................................................................

....................................................................................................................................................

....................................................................................................................................................

One disadvantage of custom-made software is .........................................................................

....................................................................................................................................................

....................................................................................................................................................

# Operating systems

1    Complete this diagram to show where the operating system works in the whole system of a device.    **(1 mark)**

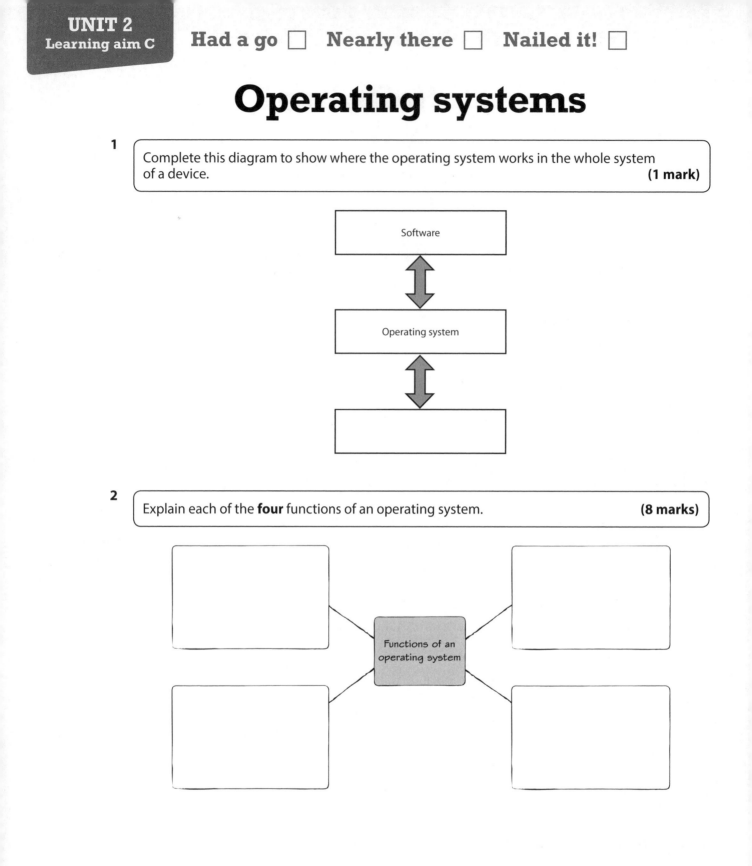

| Software |
| --- |

| Operating system |
| --- |

| |
| --- |

2    Explain each of the **four** functions of an operating system.    **(8 marks)**

Functions of an operating system

# Utility applications

**1**
Describe the purpose of a utility application.                                    **(1 mark)**

.................................................................................................................................

**2**
**(a)** Identify the utility application shown below.                             **(1 mark)**

.................................................................................................................................

**(b)** Explain what it does and why it needs to perform this task.              **(4 marks)**

.................................................................................................................................

.................................................................................................................................

.................................................................................................................................

.................................................................................................................................

**3**   Anti-virus software and firewalls can both prevent viruses.

Choose the correct terms for each and put them in the table below.              **(2 marks)**

| Anti-virus | Firewall |
|---|---|
|  |  |
|  |  |

| |
|---|
| Monitors data moving in and out of a network |
| Scans a computer to identify infected files |
| Blocks unwanted traffic such as a virus |
| Quarantines infected files which cannot be cleaned |

In the onscreen test, this question would ask you to drag and drop the terms into the correct sides of the table.

# User interfaces

1

> Draw connecting lines to match each user interface with **two** operating systems.
>
> **(4 marks)**

| Command Line Interface |

| Graphical User Interface |

| Mac OS X |
| Unix |
| MS-DOS |
| Google Chrome OS |

⟩ **Guided** ⟩  2   A software manufacturer is developing a new operating system.

> **(a)** Complete the table below comparing GUI and CLI so they can decide which one
>   to use.  **(4 marks)**

| Type of interface | GUI | CLI |
|---|---|---|
| Description | | Command Line Interface uses a simple monochrome display and no images, just text. It often only receives input from a computer and not a mouse. |
| Benefits | | |

The software manufacturer is going to develop a tablet version of their operating system.

> **(b)** Identify **two** features of the operating system which will be more important in the
>   mobile version than their PC version.  **(2 marks)**

....................................................................................................................................................

....................................................................................................................................................

# Software installation and upgrades

**1**

Which **one** of these is a productivity application? **(1 mark)**

**A** ☐ Operating system

**B** ☐ Word processor

**C** ☐ Anti-virus software

**D** ☐ System clock

**2** A college is thinking of changing its current VLE (virtual learning environment) to a different one. This new VLE has more functionality and is completely cloud-based.

Explain the following **three** issues that they need to consider before switching VLEs. **(6 marks)**

| Issue | Explanation |
|---|---|
| Cost | |
| Security | |
| Compatibility with current hardware | |

**3**

**(a)** Describe the main purpose of each of these productivity applications. **(3 marks)**

| Application | Main purpose |
|---|---|
| Spreadsheets | |
| Databases | |
| Desktop publishing (DTP) | |

**(b)** Identify **one** reason why a user would buy these applications in a suite rather than individually. **(1 mark)**

..................................................................................................................................

# Programming concepts

**1**

> What is machine code written in?      **(1 mark)**

**A** ☐   Mnemonics

**B** ☐   Natural language

**C** ☐   Hexadecimal

**D** ☐   Binary

**Guided**   **2**

> Explain why languages like C++, Java and Visual Basic (VB.Net) are considered to be high-level languages.      **(2 marks)**

High-level languages are similar to natural language, which means ...............................................

..........................................................................................................................................................

..........................................................................................................................................................

**3**

> Complete this diagram to show how high-level and low-level languages become machine code.      **(2 marks)**

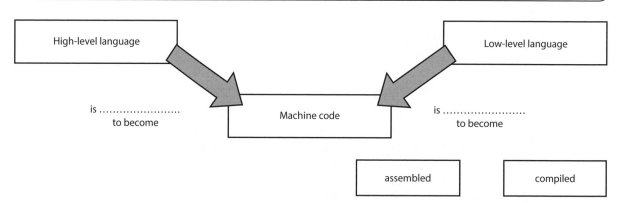

# Programming languages

**1** Match each type of language to **two** characteristics of these languages   **(4 marks)**

| High-level languages |
| Low-level languages |

| Powerful and easy to understand |
| Take up less memory space |
| Run quickly |
| More intuitive |

**2** What is assembly language usually written in?   **(1 mark)**

**A** ☐ Mnemonics

**B** ☐ Natural language

**C** ☐ Hexadecimal

**D** ☐ Binary

**Guided**

**3** Explain what mnemonics are and why they are used in low-level language programming.   **(4 marks)**

Mnemonics are abbreviations which ...................................................................................................

..............................................................................................................................................................

..............................................................................................................................................................

..............................................................................................................................................................

**4** Complete these descriptions of procedural, event-driven and object-orientated programs.   **(3 marks)**

Procedural programs have [            ] start and end points and run in a sequence.

| fixed     variable     random     several |

Event-driven programs [            ] for an event such as a mouse click and then carry out the appropriate action.

| look     listen     feel     search |

Object-orientated programs are a collection of [            ] such as a database record.

| patterns     entities     items     objects |

# Flow charts 1

**1**    What must all flow charts begin with?     **(1 mark)**

**A** ☐    Start process

**B** ☐    Start terminator

**C** ☐    Start decision

**D** ☐    Start connector

**2**    Complete this flowchart which shows the order of the processes when making an online purchase in a typical online ordering system.     **(3 marks)**

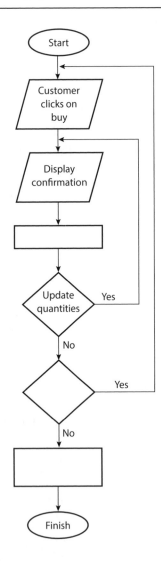

# Flow charts 2

> **Guided**

**1** Identify these flow chart symbols. **(4 marks)**

| Flow chart symbol | Name of symbol |
|---|---|
| | Process |
| | |
| | |
| | |

**2** Complete this flow chart, which shows a simple video game, by drawing the appropriate symbols. **(3 marks)**

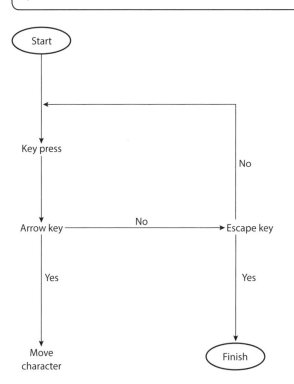

In the onscreen test, you may be asked to select the suitable symbols or to drag them onto the flow chart.

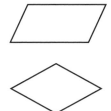

**63**

# Programming – terminology

**1**

What term describes this statement:

$$score = 10;$$

**(1 mark)**

**A** ☐   Assignment

**B** ☐   Declaration

**C** ☐   Sub-routine

**D** ☐   Input

**2**

Complete the labels on this line of code to identify the different parts of the statement.

**(3 marks)**

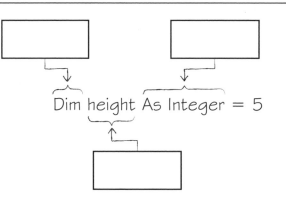

Dim height As Integer = 5

**3**

In the code below, highlight where the sub-routine begins and where it is called from the main code.

**(2 marks)**

```
Dim a As Integer
Dim b As Integer
Dim total As Integer

calculate()

MessageBox. Show (total)

Public Function (calculate)

total = a+b

End Function
```

# Programming – data types

**1** Which **one** of these will store 1.75? **(1 mark)**

A ☐ Integer

B ☐ Boolean

C ☐ Character

D ☐ Real

**2** In this example pseudocode, what happens when there is smoke? **(1 mark)**

IF hot = true THEN

Turn on sprinkler

ELSE IF smoke = true THEN

Sound alarm

END IF

.................................................................................................................................................................

**Guided** **3** What is Boolean data? Using an example, show how it might be used. **(2 marks)**

Boolean data can store a value of either true or false. This means ...........................................

.................................................................................................................................................................

.................................................................................................................................................................

.................................................................................................................................................................

# Programming – data structures

**1**

> How is the first element of an array identified? **(1 mark)**

**A** ☐ 0

**B** ☐ 1

**C** ☐ A

**D** ☐ a

**Guided** **2**

> Describe the data structure of data stored in a database. **(3 marks)**

In a database data is stored as records that are in tables. One record is ..............................

................................................................................................................................................

................................................................................................................................................

**3** This table shows an array of zoo animals.

| 0 | 1 | 2 | 3 | 4 | 5 | 6 |
|---|---|---|---|---|---|---|
| Lion | Giraffe | Penguin | Elephant | Tiger | Monkey | Peacock |

> **(a)** Complete this line of code to declare the array in the table. **(1 mark)**

Dim zoo As Array [          ]

> **(b)** Identify the data at ZOO [4] **(1 mark)**

................................................................................................................................................

> **(c)** If this array was sorted alphabetically which animal would be first? **(1 mark)**

................................................................................................................................................

**4** Lynda is creating a program for a game of chess.

> What data structure should she use? Justify your choice. **(2 marks)**

................................................................................................................................................

................................................................................................................................................

# Exam skills 1

**1** Convert this 8-bit binary number to whole numbers (base 10). **(1 mark)**

| 11010111 | |
|----------|--|

In the onscreen test system, you will have access to a calculator for questions like this.

**2** Put these boxes in order to show how languages communicate with hardware. **(3 marks)**

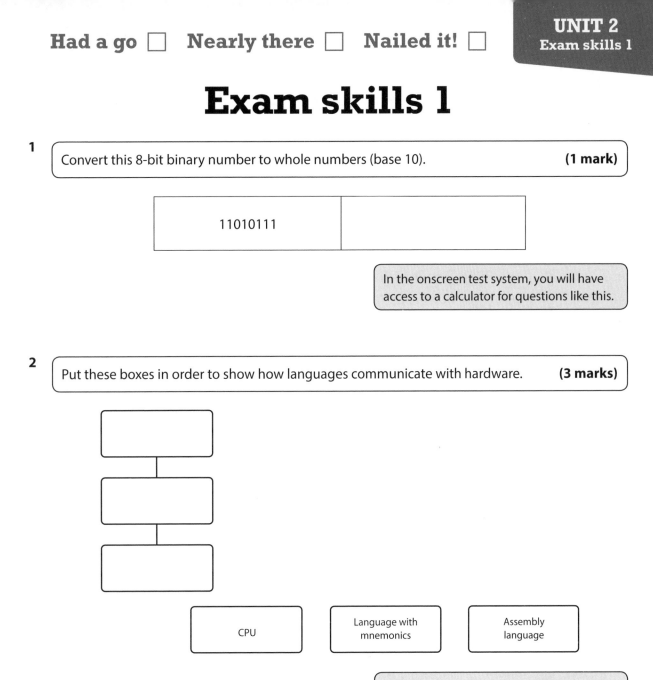

| CPU |

| Language with mnemonics |

| Assembly language |

In the onscreen test you would be able to drag and drop the terms into the boxes.

# Exam skills 2

**1**

> Clock speed determines the speed of which component? **(1 mark)**

**A** ☐ Hard drive

**B** ☐ RAM

**C** ☐ PSU

**D** ☐ CPU

**2**

> Identify which characteristics from the list below refer to low-level or high-level languages. **(4 marks)**

| Close to natural language |
|---|
| Turned into machine code very quickly |
| Easier to learn |
| Programs take up less memory |

| High-level languages | Low-level languages |
|---|---|
|  |  |
|  |  |

> In the onscreen test, you would be able to drag the list items into the boxes.

**3**

> Match the labels with the appropriate storage mediums. **(3 marks)**

Hard disk drive                    Magnetic storage media

USB memory stick                   Optical media

DVD                                Solid state media

# Exam skills 3

1   Identify different places where SRAM and DRAM would be used. Give **one** answer for **each** type of memory                                                                    **(2 marks)**

| SRAM | |
|------|--|
| DRAM | |

2   Describe **two** uses of technology in the health sector.                                **(4 marks)**

...........................................................................................................................................

...........................................................................................................................................

...........................................................................................................................................

...........................................................................................................................................

...........................................................

...........................................................

> You have been asked for two uses and the question is worth four marks – for each one give an expansion such as 'because…' or 'for example…'

3   Discuss the benefits and drawbacks of off-the-shelf software.                         **(8 marks)**

...........................................................................................................................................

...........................................................................................................................................

...........................................................................................................................................

...........................................................................................................................................

...........................................................................................................................................

...........................................................................................................................................

...........................................................................................................................................

...........................................................................................................................................

...........................................

...........................................

> Think about how you structure your answer. Plan it on paper first. Think about discussing two positives and two negatives – then expand on those four points.

# Unit 1: Practice assessment test

**You have 1 hour to complete this test.**

**The total number of marks is 50.**

### Instructions

- Use **black** ink or ballpoint pen.
- Answer **all** questions.
- Answer the questions in the spaces provided.

1 Shannon is a music festival planner and is organising the bands and artists who are going to appear.

> **(a)** Which **one** of the following is a **not** an email protocol? **(1 mark)**

A ☐ IMAP     B ☐ FTP

C ☐ POP3     D ☐ SMTP

> **(b)** Describe **two** features of email that Shannon can use in her work. **(4 marks)**

......................................................................................................................................

......................................................................................................................................

......................................................................................................................................

......................................................................................................................................

> **(c)** Identify **one** risk of which she should be aware when using email. **(1 mark)**

......................................................................................................................................

2

> Match the transmission mode with the direction of data. **(3 marks)**

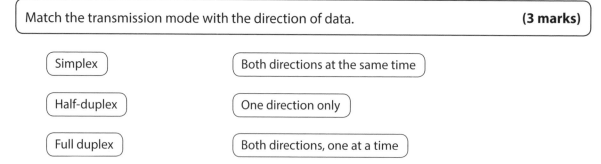

Simplex                    Both directions at the same time

Half-duplex                One direction only

Full duplex                Both directions, one at a time

3 Ismail runs a website selling gardening equipment.

> **(a)** What type of online service is this website? **(1 mark)**

A ☐ Real-time     B ☐ Government

C ☐ Education     D ☐ Commerce

**(b)** Describe **one** type of online advertising which Ismail might use to promote his business.

**(2 marks)**

...................................................................................................................................................

...................................................................................................................................................

...................................................................................................................................................

...................................................................................................................................................

4   A database at a dentists' practice uses this structure in their database.

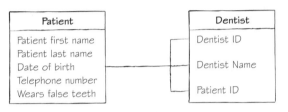

**(a)** Identify the keys in this diagram

**(3 marks)**

| Field name | Table name | Type of key |
|------------|------------|-------------|
| Patient ID | Patient | |
| Dentist ID | Dentist | |
| Patient ID | Dentist | |

**(b)** Suggest suitable data types for these fields

**(4 marks)**

| Field name | Data type |
|------------|-----------|
| Patient last name | |
| Date of birth | |
| Wears false teeth | |
| Telephone number | |

**5**

**(a)** Explain the term 'online community'. **(2 marks)**

..................................................................................................................................

..................................................................................................................................

**(b)** Give **one** example of good netiquette. **(1 mark)**

..................................................................................................................................

**6** Katrina is a secretary who works in an office on a networked computer.

Describe **two** potential risks of using her computer in her job and **two** prevention methods which could protect her from these risks. **(6 marks)**

..................................................................................................................................

..................................................................................................................................

..................................................................................................................................

..................................................................................................................................

..................................................................................................................................

..................................................................................................................................

**7** Albert's Burgers is a fast food restaurant with branches in several different countries.

**(a)** Describe what VoIP is and how it works. **(4 marks)**

..................................................................................................................................

..................................................................................................................................

..................................................................................................................................

..................................................................................................................................

**(b)** Explain **two** advantages of VoIP to Albert's Burgers. **(4 marks)**

..................................................................................................................................

..................................................................................................................................

..................................................................................................................................

..................................................................................................................................

**8** 
Complete the below table about file permissions. **(3 marks)**

| File permission | Description |
|---|---|
| Read-only access | |
| Read/Write access | |
| Full control | |

**9** 
Write the HTML for **jupiter.jpg** to open the webpage **www.planets.co.uk/jupiter/** when clicked. **(3 marks)**

...................................................................................................................................................

...................................................................................................................................................

...................................................................................................................................................

**10** Angelita is at university studying for a degree. She is considering using cloud storage for her work.

Discuss the advantages and disadvantages of her using this. **(8 marks)**

...................................................................................................................................................

...................................................................................................................................................

...................................................................................................................................................

...................................................................................................................................................

...................................................................................................................................................

...................................................................................................................................................

...................................................................................................................................................

...................................................................................................................................................

...................................................................................................................................................

# Unit 2: Practice assessment test

**You have 1 hour to complete this test.**

**The total number of marks is 50.**

**Instructions**

- Use **black** ink or ballpoint pen.
- Answer **all** questions.
- Answer the questions in the spaces provided.

1   FizzWhizz is a fizzy drinks manufacturer that produces a million cans per week. They use an automated production line to wash the cans, fill them and seal them, then put them into boxes. They use sensors to identify if the empty cans are in the right place for filling.

**(a)** What is a sensor?                                                                                  **(1 mark)**

A ☐   An input device

B ☐   An output device

C ☐   A  storage device

**(b)** Explain how sensors and robots will operate together in FizzWhizz's automated production line.                                                                             **(4 marks)**

.......................................................................................................................................

.......................................................................................................................................

.......................................................................................................................................

.......................................................................................................................................

**(c)** Describe **one** advantage of using an automated system in a production line.        **(2 marks)**

.......................................................................................................................................

.......................................................................................................................................

2   Identify suitable data types for these variables in a program                        **(3 marks)**

| Variable | Data type |
|---|---|
| Car reg | |
| Has valid MOT | |
| Top speed | |

**3**   Saqib works for a local hospital and is responsible for buying software for all of its computers.

> **(a)** Which **one** of these is an example of a productivity application?    **(1 mark)**

**A** ☐   Disk defragmenter

**B** ☐   Anti-virus software

**C** ☐   Spreadsheet

**D** ☐   Operating system

> **(b)** Saqib needs to buy software for the hospital to use to record which medicines have been prescribed to patients. Complete the table to compare the benefits of off-the-shelf and custom-made software.    **(4 marks)**

| | **Off-the-shelf** | **Custom-made** |
|---|---|---|
| Benefit 1 | | |
| Benefit 2 | | |

**4**

> **(a)** Match each characteristic to high-level or low-level languages.    **(2 marks)**

High-level languages

Low-level languages

| |
|---|
| Similar to natural language |
| Produces a relatively small file size |
| Assembles more quickly into machine code |
| Easier to learn |

> **(b)** Compare procedural and event-driven programming.    **(4 marks)**

| Procedural | Event-driven |
|---|---|
| | |

**5**

Using an example, describe a programmable digital device.   **(2 marks)**

.................................................................................................................................

.................................................................................................................................

**6**  Stacey wants to buy a new hard drive for her PC. She is considering getting either a hard disk drive or a solid state drive.

Explain the key features and differences between the two types of storage.   **(6 marks)**

.................................................................................................................................

.................................................................................................................................

.................................................................................................................................

.................................................................................................................................

.................................................................................................................................

.................................................................................................................................

**7**  A university uses a network and all devices can connect to it.

**(a)** Identify **two** uses of a network   **(2 marks)**

1 ...............................................................................................................................

2 ...............................................................................................................................

**(b)** Describe **two** benefits of using a network.   **(4 marks)**

.................................................................................................................................

.................................................................................................................................

.................................................................................................................................

.................................................................................................................................

**8**

Complete this table to show the binary and denary versions of numbers.   **(3 marks)**

| Binary (base 2) | Denary (base 10) |
|---|---|
| 00000111 |  |
|  | 5 |
| 11011011 |  |

**9**

**(a)** Complete this diagram showing internal components of a PC.    **(2 marks)**

```
                    ┌──────────┐
                    │ Storage  │
                    └──────────┘
                      ↑      ↓
┌────────┐          ┌──────────┐          ┌────────┐
│ Input  │ ───────→ │   RAM    │ ───────→ │ Output │
└────────┘          └──────────┘          └────────┘
                      ↑      ↓
            ┌────────────────────────┐
            │         CPU            │
            │   ┌────────────────┐   │
            │   │      ALU       │   │
            │   ├────────────────┤   │
            │   │                │   │
            │   └────────────────┘   │
            │   ┌────────────────┐   │
            │   │                │   │
            │   └────────────────┘   │
            └────────────────────────┘
```

**(b)** What is the function of the ALU?    **(1 mark)**

.....................................................................................................................................................

**(c)** What is the function of the Registers?    **(1 mark)**

.....................................................................................................................................................

**10**

Discuss the functions of an operating system.    **(8 marks)**

.....................................................................................................................................................

.....................................................................................................................................................

.....................................................................................................................................................

.....................................................................................................................................................

.....................................................................................................................................................

.....................................................................................................................................................

.....................................................................................................................................................

.....................................................................................................................................................

# Answers

The following pages contain example answers for questions in the Workbook. In many cases, they represent only one possible correct answer.

## Unit 1

### LEARNING AIM A

### 1. Online services 1

1  **D** Online tax returns

2  An example of a real-time online service is a live departure and arrival website for an airport. It is real-time because it always needs to be kept up-to-date with the latest information on flight times.

3  Commerce online services involve money. One example of an online commerce service is a retail website where products are sold over the internet, such as a website selling DVDs to customers. Another example is an online bank, which also involves money.

4  **A** Communication

### 2. Online services 2

1  VLE stands for Virtual Learning Environment. It is used in schools and colleges by both teachers and students. Teachers can upload learning materials and create quizzes. Students can submit their work through the VLE.

2  Online download services can access music and software (or films). [Many answers possible]

3  **A** Video conferencing.

4  Education: Online learning and Virtual learning environment
Business: Video conferencing and internet banking

### 3. Online advertising

1  **B** Pay-per-click

2  A sponsored link is listed at the top of search results, which makes it more visible and more likely for a user to click on it.

3  Pop-up adverts often include animation, video and audio. They can be annoying because they distract from the actual website content they are accessing.

4  Methods of online advertising include banner adverts, pop-up adverts, search engine results and email marketing. Online promotion allows access to those who are active online, which is good for businesses who have an internet presence. Online advertising can attract attention by using animation, colours and graphics. Email marketing goes direct into users' inboxes. Pay-per-click advertising can be placed on similar websites to attract customers who are already interested in similar products, e.g. good targeting of potential customers.

### 4. Online documents – file compression

1  **C** Zipping

2  Anya's email may have a limit as to the size of attachment which can be sent. Compressing the file will make it smaller so it is under the limit.

3  A file is compressed using an algorithm. To decompress a file, the index is used to put the file back to its original form.

4  Any two of the following: Editing out unnecessary parts of the video, splitting it into a number of pieces, using more than one memory stick, changing the format, compressing the file.

### 5. Online software and backups

1  A backup is a copy of data saved in a different location.

2  Standalone software is installed onto the device's hard drive, whereas online software is accessed over an internet connection and not installed.

3  (a)  Reha and her team could save money by not buying expensive computers with large hard drives and other data storage because all of the data will be stored on the cloud. They can also access it anywhere there is an internet connection, so they can work outside the office as well, such as on the train or when they are meeting clients.

   (b)  One risk is security, as anything online can be at risk from hackers and viruses. Another risk is reliance on an external company, as if the host servers are unavailable the software becomes unavailable.

### 6. Collaborative working online

1  Version control is important so that you know you are working on the most up-to-date version of a document.

2  Collaborative working tools can be accessed via the internet, so people can work on the same documents even though they are in different countries.

3  (a)

| Person | Level of access | Actions allowed |
|--------|-----------------|-----------------|
| Brandon | Read-only | Can view the customer records but not edit them |
| Lydia | Read/Write | Can view customer records and edit them, but not delete them |
| Shaheeb | Full control | Can view, edit and delete customers records |

   (b)  Training

### 7. Online communication 1

1  **B** Members of the wiki (people who have signed up)

2  Blog = An online journal
Podcast = A regular downloadable audio file

3  An online chatroom means that people can chat live (real-time) like a conversation.
A forum is where users can leave messages so other users can access the messages when it is convenient for them.

4  (a)  An online community is a group of people, usually with similar interests, which exists online.

   (b)  The business could build an online community using a social networking site and this could allow the business to build their brand through word-of-mouth and increased dedication from their customers (and therefore potentially more profit).

## 8. Online communication 2

1  **B** Typing in capitals

2  Avatar, username, emoticons

3

| Username | JohnnySmith | Although the user has given a name, it cannot be trusted this is their true name. |
|---|---|---|
| Age | 14 | They have given their age as a teenager but they may not be this age and could actually be an adult. |
| Location | <the same region as you> | They have said they are in the same region to you – the risk is that they might suggest to meet. Can you believe this is true? |

## 9. Voice over Internet Protocol

1  **D** IP address

2  VoIP sends voice/audio/video data

3  Microphone and webcam

4  VoIP can be used in businesses to hold meetings with employees at branches in different countries. An advantage of this is that they can have meetings even though they are in different locations. This can save money and time in travelling. Another way VoIP can be used in business is for collaborative working, which is where employees can work on the same project at the same time. VoIP is better than discussing over just text (such as email) or voice (such as telephone). Some VoIP programs can also allow users to show documents on screen so they can work together on it.

One disadvantage is reliability because if the connection over the internet is lost, then the communication will stop. Another disadvantage is security as a hacker could intercept the data and this is bad if the data is private to the business.

## 10. Cloud computing

1  **B** External servers

2  Web browser (on a computer) and web app (on a mobile device)

3  **(a)** One way that cloud computing could benefit Tony is that it is available anywhere where there is an internet connection, so he can access his files when he is travelling and visiting his clients. Another way the cloud could benefit Tony is that he can buy a lighter device, perhaps a tablet, because he does not need a large hard drive to store data and this will be easier to carry around.

**(b)** One disadvantage is reliability because if the internet connection is unavailable or weak then Tony will not be able to access his files. A second disadvantage is that Tony is relying on the security of the external servers and this is important as he is saving important business files on the cloud and would not want his competitors to have access to them.

## 11. Ubiquitous computing

1  **A** RFID

2  Ubiquitous computing is where processors are embedded in everyday objects.

3

| Household appliances | Ubiquitous computing can be processors embedded in washing machines to control how the clothes are washed. |
|---|---|
| Animals or people | People may have a pacemaker put inside them to make their heart beat regularly. |
| Shopping | Security tags with RFID chips inside are put on products like clothes and sensors near all of the exits in a shop to prevent them from being stolen. |

4  If the company puts tracking devices on their vehicles, then the owners will know where their cars are at all times. Also, the coordinators taking phone calls and organising which taxis go where will be better able to arrange the cars, giving a better service for their customers. They may be able to use the devices to check that taxi drivers are taking the best routes.

## LEARNING AIM B

### 12. The internet – hardware

1  The internet is a network of interconnected computers all around the world.

2  Server, router, client

3  ISP stands for Internet Service Provider. An ISP allows users to connect to the internet by providing a gateway which would be too difficult or expensive to do without it. ISPs also provide other services such as help with website development and email.

### 13. The internet – network diagrams

1  PoP (Point of Presence)

2  ISP, client

3  Internet, router

### 14. Connection methods

1

| Internet connection method | Description |
|---|---|
| Wireless | Connected without wires |
| Dial-up | Wired connection through a telephone line |

2  High bandwidth means that more data can move through a cable per second. The more data that can move through the cable means that a website is downloaded to a client more quickly and appears in the browser.

3  **(a)** An advantage of dial-up is that it uses existing telephone lines so it would be good if Abi was based where other services were not available. However, older technology can give poor reception and sometimes there are errors in conversion between digital and analogue signals. Also it is usually slower than other methods.

**(b)** If Abi wants to go wireless, this has the advantage that she could use mobile devices such as a laptop or tablet, as it is not fixed to a stationary computer. Her devices would need a wireless network interface card (NIC) in order to connect. However, wireless can be less secure and tends to be slower than a wired broadband connection.

### 15. The internet – protocols

1  A protocol is a set of rules that allow different computers and devices to communicate over a network.

2  **(a)** **B** IP and **D** TCP

**(b)** **A** Packet switching

3

| Protocol | Main purpose |
|---|---|
| TCP | TCP takes data from the user's application and passes it to IP for transfer across the internet. It organises data into packets. |
| IP | IP finds routes for the data packets to travel across the internet. |
| FTP | FTP allows files to be transferred between computers/devices. |

## 16. World Wide Web

1  Web browsers display web pages.
Web servers store web pages.

2  A user requests a web page using a web address/URL.
A copy of the web page is then downloaded from the web server to the client's computer. It is viewed through a web browser.

3  (a)  Hyperlinks

(b)  A user clicks on a hyperlink and it loads a different web page or document.

## 17. HTML

1  **D** A language

2  <a href=www.candles.com>Buy candles here</a>

3

| HTML | Displayed on web page |
|---|---|
| <i>Sunflower</i> | *Sunflower* |
| Daffodil | **Daffodil** |
| <li><br><ul> Daisy </ul><br><ul> Dandelion </ul><br><ul> Bluebell </ul><br></li> | • Daisy<br>• Dandelion<br>• Bluebell |

## 18. URLs

1  (a)  Uniform Resource Locator

(b)  A web address that points to an individual web page

2  Hypertext Transfer Protocol

3  http:// = protocol
lancashiremuseums.co.uk = domain name
visit/january/ = path

4  HTTP will load the PDF into a web browser. FTP will download the PDF document at that location.

## 19. Search engines

1  (a)  **B** Bugs

(b)  New or updated content on web pages

(c)  In the search engine's database

(d)  **A** All the time

2

| Sponsored link |
|---|
| Most popular result |
| Less popular result |

3

| User enters key words |
|---|
| The database is searched |
| Results are displayed |

## 20. Email – purposes and uses

1  **C** BCC, **D** CC

2  Reply, Reply to all and Forward

3  Clockwise from top: attachment, priority, subject

4  One of the advantages of email for David is that he can send attachments with his emails. This means if he has photographs he can attach them to emails and send them to the news desk. Another advantage is that he can send emails to multiple recipients at the same time so he could send an email to his news desk and other contacts. One disadvantage is that there is a security risk. If David has a good story then he would not want a hacker to steal the story and give it to a competitor, and email is at risk because it is sent over the internet. Another disadvantage is that email can only be sent if there is internet connection and if David is reporting from a place where there is no internet available he will not be able to email the news desk.

## 21. Email – protocols

1  Webmail

2  SMTP – Push
POP3 – Pull

3  Usma could set up a webmail account for free, the only cost being that of the internet connection. She would be able to access her webmail anywhere that there is an internet connection. Usma could set up a web mail account to use in all locations because webmail is stored on the cloud and is the same wherever it is accessed. However, if she finds that on placement she does not have internet access she will not be able to access her webmail.

## 22. Data exchange – packet switching

1  **C** Route instructions

2  Packet switching is used to send data across a network efficiently because the data is in small packets and can choose different routes through the network. In addition, there is also a security benefit because if the data is intercepted, the hacker will only have one part of the whole file.

3  A drawback to packet switching is that if one or more packets are lost or corrupted during transmission, the whole file will not be received correctly.

4

| Data packet parts | Description |
|---|---|
| Packet identification | Gives each packet an ID so it can be identified when it is to be put back together |
| Destination address | Location of the recipient's computer |
| Source address | Location of the sender's computer |
| Payload | The data being carried by the packet |
| Error control bits | This checks that the packets have been reassembled correctly – it checks for errors |

## 23. Data exchange – transmission modes

1  **B** Half-simplex

2  (a)  A serial transmission mode sends bits of data one at a time over a cable and it is reassembled once transferred.

(b)  Parallel is a faster transmission mode because bytes of data (8 bits) are transferred over the cable at the same time, instead of one bit at a time.

| 3 | Transmission mode | Direction | Example device |
|---|---|---|---|
| | Full-duplex | Both directions at the same time | Mobile phone |
| | Half-duplex | Both directions, one at a time | Printer |
| | Simplex | One direction only | Radio broadcast |

### 24. Wired transmission methods

1  **C** To cancel out interference

2  UTP is unshielded whereas STP is shielded. The shield is between the twisted copper wire and plastic casing and protects from further interference.

3  UTP = Susceptible to noise
Coaxial = Slowest and lowest capacity
Fibre optic = Most expensive to install

4  Fibre optic is an appropriate type to use for the backbone because it is a fast method of transmission for the backbone of the office. It has a high data capacity because the cables use light to transfer data instead of copper wires. It works over long distances, such as around the office block, because light can carry data further than copper wires, which will degrade over 100 metres.

STP is an appropriate type to connect each computer to the backbone because it is cheaper than other wired cables, flexible and has a good data transfer rate. Twisting inside the cable cancels out interference. The shielding is an extra protective layer in the cable (which UTP does not have) and cancels out more interference. STP cables can be easily replaced if they are damaged.

### 25. Wireless transmission methods

1  **D** Microwaves

| 2 | Wireless transmission methods | Approximate data transfer rate | Approximate range |
|---|---|---|---|
| | Infrared | 4 Mbps | 10 m |
| | Microwave | 100 Mbps | 100 m |
| | Satellite | 100 Gbps | 20,000 km |

3  A benefit of wireless is that they could offer free wireless to their customers. The effect on the business might be increased customers as they have a competitive advantage and may attract brand new customers who have not previously used the café. The limitations include the cost as they will need to buy the equipment for a wireless signal and also pay for a suitable internet connection from their ISP. In addition they will need to consider the legal and ethical implications because they may be implicated if one of their customers uses their connection to access unsavoury or illegal material.

### 26. Client-side processing

1  The client's processor

2  Client-side processing can produce **interactivity** on a web page.

When a web page is requested, a copy is **downloaded** onto the client's computer.

This is created on the web page using **code/script**.

3  An advantage of client-side processing is that the retailer can gain the advantage of speed. Once the website material has downloaded onto the client's computer it can process faster without data needing to move backwards and

forwards over the internet. Another advantage of client-side processing is security, because there is less moving data across the internet, which means there is less risk of it being intercepted by hackers.

One disadvantage of client-side processing for the retailer is that it is browser specific, which means that it depends on what type of browser the client is using as to how it is shown onscreen because each browser interprets scripts differently. Another disadvantage is that they are relying on the processor speed of the client, as that is where it will be processed and if that is slow then the website may appear to be slow.

### 27. Server-side processing

1  The web server's processor

2  **(a)** Browser-specific means that the way the data is processed depends on the browser being used. Each browser interprets scripts differently.

**(b)** Client-side scripting occurs on the client, therefore is dependent on the type of browser being used by the client. Server-side scripting occurs on the web server, therefore no browser is involved in the processing.

3  An advantage of server-side processing for the retailer is efficiency because it is processed on the server rather than having to download it onto the client.

Another advantage of server-side processing is that it is browser independent so it doesn't matter what browser the client is using, as it occurs on the web server.

### 28. Database theory

1  record          table          fields

| 2 | Field | Data type |
|---|---|---|
| | Last name | Text |
| | Date of birth | Date/time |
| | Postcode | Text |
| | Mobile number | Text |

3  **(a)** Customer ID in Customer = primary key
Customer ID in Car = foreign key
Car registration in Car = primary key

**(b)** one-to-many

### 29. Databases in practice

1  **B** SQL

2  In a DBMS DDL (Data Definition Language) defines the structure of the database. DML (Data Manipulation Language) controls adding, deleting and editing data. It also controls querying the data.

3  A query searches the data in the database.

4  An online database means that it can be accessed from anywhere where there is an internet connection, which would give a lot of freedom of movement for the retailer. They may be able to use free software, which would reduce the costs for the company. In addition, the hosting company often offer additional features and support, which may be helpful to the retailer if they have limited ability in their staff.

### LEARNING AIM C

### 30. Threats to data

1  A computer virus will try to be disruptive or damaging. It can damage or delete data, or share it with the purpose of identity theft and other bad purposes.

2  Phishing means an email or website pretending to be real but which is actually fake.

**3 (a)** Damage from an untrained user

**(b)** Accidental damage is an accident and not meant to happen. An opportunist threat sees an opportunity and acts on it. An opportunist threats means to cause damage or steal data.

## 31. Protection of data

**1** More than eight characters, capital letter, number, symbol

**2** Lock doors, CCTV cameras, turn computers off at night

**3**

| Threat | Prevention method | Explanation of prevention method |
|---|---|---|
| Virus | Anti-virus software | Monitors files and deletes viruses or quarantines infected files |
| Hackers | Firewall | Monitors data going in and out of the network |
| | Encryption | Encodes data so if it is stolen it cannot be understood |
| New, untrained members of staff | Levels of access | Restricts access to only the data they need to view or edit. |

**4** If the threat is not prevented, it could mean that data is corrupted or deleted. If the data has been backed up, then it can be recovered and put back to how it was before.

## 32. Legislation

**1** Data Protection Act 1998

**2 1** Hackers

   **2** Viruses

**3** Geoff may use a service like iTunes or Spotify, which allows him to download music to his devices in return for a subscription fee. If he stops paying his subscription, the music will be deleted from his devices automatically. Katherine downloads music illegally, which means that she is breaking the Copyright, Designs and Patents Act 1988, which gives ownership of music (and other creative works) to the creator. If Katherine is caught she could be fined or even imprisoned, depending on the quantity of music she has downloaded and if she has shared it with or sold it to anyone else.

## 33. Exam skills 1

**1** **A** UTP and **C** coaxial

**2** Manager = Full access, Solicitor = Read/write access, Secretary = Read only

**3**

| Error control bits | Payload | Source address | Destination address | Packet identification |
|---|---|---|---|---|

## 34. Exam skills 2

**1** **B** Client

**2** Employees can send messages to multiple people at the same time and Employees can access contacts in their address book

**3**

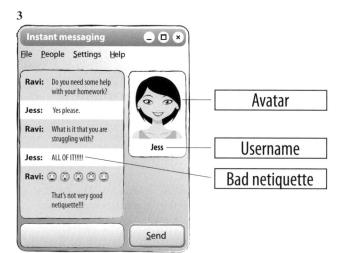

## 35. Exam skills 3

**1** Serial – sends one bit at a time
Parallel – sends one byte (8 bits) at a time

**2** One threat is a hacker who could try to get unauthorized access to a network or data. Another threat is a virus, which is a malicious program that will replicate and try to damage or steal data.

**3** Cloud computing uses external servers to store data rather than the local hard disk drive.

One benefit is cost because you do not need to buy an expensive hard drive to store large amounts of data.

Another benefit is that it is available anywhere where there is an internet connection, rather than just on one computer.

One drawback is you are relying on the security of the external company and if they do not have good security your data could be damaged or stolen.

Another drawback is that if the external servers go down and are not available, you will not be able to access your data.

Unit 2

**LEARNING AIM A**

**36. Technology systems**

1 **C** Manufacturing

2 In the health sector x-rays are taken digitally and stored on large databases so that doctors can access x-rays from any computer and they can be archived forever.

3 Bar code scanning

4 Faster transaction/queuing time

5 Any two of the following: Reduced cost, increased accuracy, immediate knowledge of what products are sold, immediate knowledge of what needs replacing on the shelves, reliable way of implementing special offers.

**37. Issues in technology systems**

1 **A** Sustainability

2 Viruses and spyware (Trojans, worms, adware, rootkit)

3 Unauthorised sources are usually hackers. Users can protect their systems by using a firewall. A firewall will monitor data in and out of a system or network and block unauthorized access. Another method of protection is to use strong passwords. These must include uppercase, lowercase, numbers and symbols and should be at least eight characters in length.

4 Smartphones are made from metals, such as tin, which need to be mined from the ground. This can damage the environment because the process uses up the earth's natural resources. Mining also uses energy and fuel and creates pollution. Additionally, the materials need to be transported and then processed into the product.

**38. Developing technology systems**

1 **D** Reduced revenue

2 Improved performance – Improving user interface of software to make it easier to use.
Competitive advantage – Improving the product so it has more functionality for the same price.
Reduced costs – Improving delivery routes which requires less petrol in the vehicles.

3 The manufacturer is developing its technology because by using robots on the production line they should be able to reduce costs. Although there may be an initial cost to purchase the robots, they will save money on salaries in the long run.
A positive impact on the company is that they may make more profit.
A negative impact on the company is that they may have to make employees redundant.

**39. Hardware devices**

1 **B** Tablet

2 A processor (CPU)

3 Samantha could use a tablet which is lighter to carry than her diary, it will give her the same functionality and more, she will not need a pen and the data will be backed up and harder to destroy.

4 (a) The GPU processes visual images and will improve the graphics and the computer's performance.

(b) As the laptop is portable, Mohammed can carry it with him and play while he is on the train or out with his friends.

(c) The laptop's internet connection will only work if he has access, therefore he will not be able to play where there is no internet connection available.

(d) The games console uses cloud storage, which will automatically back up his game. It also means he can connect anywhere where there is an internet connection and access his saved games.

**40. Input and output**

1 Input → Process → Output

2 **D** Projector

3 A touch screen is used for input on a smartphone because the user can touch the screen with their finger. The device records where they touched and sends a signal to the processor (system on chip – SoC), which then takes an action depending where on screen they press. A touch screen can also be an output device because, like a monitor, it displays information on the screen.

4 Actuator – Radio-controlled car
Microphone – Video conferencing
Sensor – Car wash
Force feedback – Games console

**41. Storage**

1 (a) **A** HDD

(b) The magnetic disk is where the data is saved. Each bit is saved either facing north or south and this represents zeros or ones in binary. The read/write head moves backwards and forwards over the disk as it rotates and reads data from it and writes (saves) data to it. It can move backwards and forwards so it can save to different sectors on the disk.

2 **Hard disk drive**
Benefit 1: Usually cheaper for the same storage capacity as SSD.
Benefit 2: Can be purchased in larger sizes than SSD.
**Solid State Drive**
Benefit 1: SSD is quieter than HDD because there are no moving parts.
Benefit 2: SSD is usually more reliable than HDD because there are no moving parts.

3 CD = A disk that has been written to and can't be changed.
CD-R = A disk that is blank and can be written to once by the user but then the data is fixed.
CD-RW = A blank CD that can be written to several times by the user.

**42. Automated systems**

1 Robots can operate in dangerous conditions when humans could not work in those situations. Robots can carry out repetitive, boring tasks and can operate consistently in almost any conditions.

2 An input device used on a production line is a sensor that will sense where an item is. Therefore, the system does not need human interaction to operate. An output device used on a production line like this is a robot arm that can automatically carry out accurate instructions stored in a computer.

**43. Devices to capture data**

1 **B** OMR

2 An OCR (Optical Character Reader).

3 An advantage of using an RFID chip is that the warehouse staff will know at all times what their stock level is therefore they will know when their stock runs out or reaches a re-order level. They will also know if an item is lost or stolen.

Another advantage of using RFID chips is that warehouse staff selecting products which have been ordered should be quicker, therefore the customer should get their order in less time than with a different system.

A disadvantage is that RFID chips are more expensive and involve printing barcodes on labels, which means that their cost will be higher and they may need to raise the price of their product. Another disadvantage is that a system needs to be purchased and installed, staff will need training and all of this will cost time and money. Regular maintenance will also be needed and this will also cost money.

### 44. Types and uses of networks

1  **B** WAN

2  Either of the following: The user would need to connect to Wi-Fi, or use a WAP (Wireless Access Point).

3  Example 1: Calendar
Example 2: Email
Example 3: Contacts
Example 4: Photos and music

4  PAN – A network that includes a few devices close to each other e.g. devices in a personal space
WAN – A network that spans several countries
LAN – A network that is in one office or building

### 45. Benefits of networks

1  **B** Security

2  Vimala and Jonathan can use email if they want to communicate by text and they can also send attachments, such as photos. Another way they can communicate is by video conferencing, such as Skype, where they can transmit audio/video data across the network.

3  Any five of the following: Saves money; better access; improves efficiency; reduces pollution by reducing the need to travel; saves time, improves communication; easier to share resources.

### 46. Methods of transferring data

1  **B** Glass

2  UTP – Connecting PCs to routers in a network
Fibre optic – Backbone of a network, connecting routers to servers
Coaxial – Connecting to a cable television network

3  A physical network is where each device is connected through a wire. An example is a classroom where the PCs are cabled into the network. This is because the PCs do not need to be moved and it gives a more reliable connection. A wireless network is one where the devices are not connected with cable and use wireless technology such as Wi-Fi. An example of this is a tablet user having access to the internet while on the move, e.g. out shopping.

### LEARNING AIM B

### 47. Main components of a computer

1  **C** CPU and **D** PSU

2  **(a)** To process data

  **(b)** Permanent memory for data storage

3  Expansion cards can be for sound or graphics. (Other answers acceptable). They provide additional functionality to the components already in the device. Originally a device may have on-board graphics or sound and you may use an expansion card to make the device more powerful.
A graphics expansion card may also have a GPU on it to process graphical information. Another use of expansion cards is for wireless networking for devices which do not have this built in.

### 48. Processing digital data 1

1  **C**. Instructions

2  **(a)** [Top] Storage, [Middle] ALU, [Bottom] Control Unit

  **(b)** ALU – comparisons and calculations
Registers – store instructions and results from the ALU
Control unit – gets data from the RAM, returns data to the RAM, makes sure that the instructions are carried out by other hardware.

### 49. Processing digital data 2

1  **C** One word

2  Cache memory is used to buffer data between a fast component and a slow component. For example, data from fast RAM can be fed into the cache memory and then more slowly fed into a slower hard drive which frees up the RAM.

3  **(a)** A data bus is a connection on a PCB (printed circuit board), such as a motherboard.

  **(b)** If you increase the number or size of a data bus then more data can be transferred, making it appear to process more quickly.

4  Quad core means that the processor has four cores which mean that it can process four instructions simultaneously. Therefore unlike a processor with a single core, which can only process one instruction at a time, a quad core processor is four times as fast.
2 GHz is the measurement of the clock cycles. For each clock cycle a processor can process one word of data. A word is a fixed number of bits, such as 54 bits. The more clock cycles a processor has the more data it can process per second therefore the faster the processor appears.

### 50. Memory and storage

1  **(a)** **C** Permanent and a type of memory

  **(b)** Either of the following: The ROM chip stores the current date and time. The ROM chips stores the boot up sequence for when the PC is turned on.

2  **(a)** Temporary means that the data held in RAM is deleted when the computer is turned off.

  **(b)** RAM is used to hold data and programs in current use.

3  **(a)** Dynamic Random Access Memory
Static Random Access Memory

4  Smartphone – SRAM
Laptop – DRAM

### 51. Mobile devices

1  **B** SoC

2  **(a)** Weight – Size – Battery life – Interface – Functionality

  **(b)** Manufacturers need to design a product that customers will like and therefore buy so they can make a profit, e.g. a phone which is light so they can carry it in their pocket. They also should make products that use new technology as it becomes available because customers will expect devices to keep improving and will not purchase old fashioned devices.

### 52. Analogue and digital data

1  Analogue data occurs in the natural world and changes with time. It is represented by an electrical signal. Digital data is a representation of a sequence of discrete values or numbers. It is stored using bits and bytes.

**2** Analogue data is sampled at regular intervals to turn it into digital data. When it is played back, the human ear fills in the 'gaps' and hears continuous sound. The more samples that are taken (closer together), the higher the quality of sound.

**3** Spoken words are analogue data.
Sound waves are sampled to create digital data.
The data can then be processed by the computer.

## 53. Converting denary to binary

**1** 0111

Workings:

| 8 | 4 | 2 | 1 | | |
|---|---|---|---|---|---|
| 0 | 1 | 1 | 1 | = | 7 |

**2** **(a)**

| 0 | 0000 |
|---|------|

**(b)**

| 1 | 0001 |
|---|------|

**(c)**

| 2 | 0010 |
|---|------|

**(d)**

| 3 | 0011 |
|---|------|

**(e)**

| 4 | 0100 |
|---|------|

**(f)**

| 5 | 0101 |
|---|------|

## 54. Converting binary to denary

**1** 10

Workings:

| 128 | 64 | 32 | 16 | ⑧ | 4 | ② | 1 | | |
|-----|----|----|----|----|---|----|---|---|---|
| 0 | 0 | 0 | 0 | 1 | 0 | 1 | 0 | = | 8 + 2 = 10 |

**2** **(a)**

| 10001100 | 140 |
|----------|-----|

**(b)**

| 10101111 | 175 |
|----------|-----|

**(c)**

| 11011101 | 221 |
|----------|-----|

**(d)**

| 01101110 | 110 |
|----------|-----|

**(e)**

| 00010001 | 17 |
|----------|-----|

**3** A word is a fixed number of bits e.g. 32-bit and 64-bit. A word is the amount of data which can be processed in the CPU at one time. The larger the word which can be processed, the faster the processing speed, therefore 64-bit processors are faster than 32-bit processors. Windows 7 has been released in two versions to use the processor more efficiently. Both versions have exactly the same functionality; however the 64-bit makes more efficient use of the processor and takes advantage of its faster speed. If a user has a 64-bit processor but installs the 32-bit version of Windows 7 it will still work but not as quickly as it could. If a user installs the 64-bit version of Windows 7 on a PC with a 32-bit processor it will not work correctly because the software will be trying to run faster than the processor can.

## LEARNING AIM C

### 55. Software

**1** Software is a program or application which can be run on a device with a processor to carry out instructions.

**2** C Off-the-shelf

**3** One advantage of off-the-shelf software is that the software is usually cheaper than custom-made because a generic product can be made and released rather than developing different versions for each company.
One disadvantage of off-the-shelf software is that it may not have the specific functionality needed by a company; for example, a manufacturing business wanting to control a production line.
One advantage of custom-made software is that it will do exactly what is needed by the client because the client can be involved during the design and development stages.
One disadvantage of custom-made software is that it can take a long time between requesting the software and being able to use it because it needs to be designed, developed and tested thoroughly.

### 56. Operating systems

**1** Hardware

**2** Managing files – allowing users to organise how they store their data by using folders and being able to rename, copy and delete files
Managing hardware – using the hardware components in the device to load programs and use drivers, such as for printers or a graphics card
Allocating resources – receiving input such as a mouse click, sending output such as accessing a printer and managing saving to the hard disk drive
Handling security issues – creating restore points which the user can revert back to, backing up data and controlling access by usernames and passwords

### 57. Utility applications

**1** A utility application is one which performs one task to improve the performance of a device.

**2** **(a)** Disk defragmenter (defrag)

**(b)** A disk defragmenter analyses the data blocks on a storage device, such as a hard drive, and organises them so files are saved in the same place and similar types of data are together. This needs to be done because when a file is deleted, it leaves a 'gap' and when another file is saved the gap will be filled but if the file is bigger than the gap the rest will be saved elsewhere on the hard drive. Fragmented files take longer to load and save and therefore the device runs slower.

**3**

| Anti-virus | Firewall |
|------------|----------|
| Scans a computer to identify infected files | Monitors data moving in and out of a network |
| Quarantines infected files which cannot be cleaned | Blocks unwanted traffic such as a virus |

## 58. User interfaces

1 Command Line Interface = MS-DOS, Unix

Graphical User Interface = Mac OS X, Google Chrome OS

2 (a)

| Type of interface | GUI | CLI |
|---|---|---|
| Description | A Graphical User Interface uses images and text to display the operating system and software to the user. It uses WIMP (windows, icons, menus and pointer) and the user can interact with input devices such as a keyboard and mouse. | Command Line Interface uses a simple monochrome display and no images, just text. It often only receives input from a keyboard and not a mouse. |
| Benefits | A GUI is easier to use, especially for non-expert users, and is intuitive and easier to learn. | A CLI runs more quickly as it does not need to process a lot of graphical information. |

(b) User interface, for example used with a touch screen. Ease of use so that the device is intuitive and users can quickly learn how to use it. Other similar answers acceptable.

## 59. Software installation and upgrades

1 **B** Word processor

2

| Issue | Explanation |
|---|---|
| Cost | If the new VLE has more functionality is it going to be more expensive than the current one? Also if a bigger internet connection is needed, this will also cost more. |
| Security | If the new VLE is saving to the cloud, will this make the security weaker as it is using the internet? Will more money need to be spent on increasing the data security? |
| Compatibility with current hardware | If the VLE is cloud-based this means more data will be moving over the internet. Is the college's internet connection big enough to cope with the increased traffic? |

3 (a)

| Application | Main purpose |
|---|---|
| Spreadsheets | Working with numbers and performing calculations, such as finances |
| Databases | Storing data in records (usually large amounts of data) which can then be searched and sorted |
| Desktop publishing (DTP) | Creating documents for publishing, such as leaflets and newsletters |

(b) A user may want to buy a suite of applications because they will all operate in a similar way, therefore less training is needed to use all of the applications.

## 60. Programming concepts

1 **D** Binary

2 High-level languages are similar to natural language which means they use words, in English or in a syntax (order of words) that is similar to a sentence.

3 High-level language is **compiled** to become machine code. Low-level language is **assembled** to become machine code.

## 61. Programming languages

1 High-level languages = powerful and easy to understand, more intuitive

Low-level languages = take up less memory space, run quickly

2 **A** Mnemonics

3 Mnemonics are abbreviations which represent instructions e.g. MOV for move and CMP for compare. They are used in low-level programming on each line of instruction; unlike high-level languages, low-level programming usually only has one instruction per line. Mnemonics are short for instruction words and, because they are small, do not take up much space when the program is saved and can be run quickly.

4 fixed – listen – objects

## 62. Flow charts 1

1 **B** Start terminator

2 Store product in shopping basket / Continue shopping? / Proceed to checkout

## 63. Flow charts 2

1

| Flow chart symbol | Name of symbol |
|---|---|
| | Process |
| | Terminator |
| | Decision box |
| | Data (input/output) |

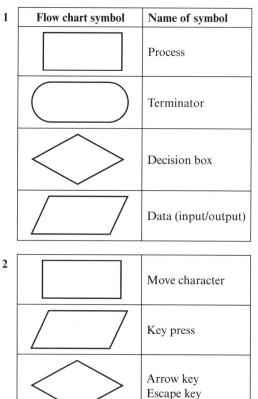

2

| | |
|---|---|
| | Move character |
| | Key press |
| | Arrow key Escape key |

## 64. Programming – terminology

1 **A** Assignment

2 Dim = declaration, height = variable, As Integer = data type

3 Sub-routine begins: Public Function (calculate) Sub-routine is called: calculate()

## 65. Programming – data types

**1** **D** Real

**2** The alarm sounds

**3** Boolean data can store a value of either true or false. This means it can be used to look at a condition and see whether an action should be carried out. For example, a Boolean called 'reorder' could be used in stock control and be set to true when the stock level reaches a certain point. An example in pseudocode might be:
IF (stocklevel <= reorderlevel) THEN reorder = true
IF (reorder = true) THEN buy more stock

## 66. Programming – data structures

**1** **A** 0

**2** In a database data is stored as records that are in tables. One record is a row in a table and holds information about a single item e.g. a customer record. A table holds data about a particular thing, e.g. customers. Tables have fields which are categories of data, e.g. name, address, phone number, etc.

**3** **(a)** Dim zoo As Array [7]

**(b)** Tiger

**(c)** Elephant

**4** Lynda should use a 2D array. This is because she can store the X and Y co-ordinates of the board in each array, so that the board can be 'mapped', and know where all of the pieces are on the board.

## 67. Exam skills 1

**1** 215

**2** Language with mnemonics – Assembly language – CPU

## 68. Exam skills 2

**1** **D** CPU

**2** High-level languages = Close to natural language, Easier to learn
Low-level languages = Turned into machine code very quickly, Programs take up less memory

**3** Hard disk drive = Magnetic storage media
USB memory stick = Solid state media
DVD = Optical media

## 69. Exam skills 3

**1** SRAM = smartphone (or digital camera or tablet)
DRAM = PC (or laptop)

**2** Technology can be used in the health sector to scan patients, for example x-ray machines can be used to look inside a patient at their bones and also store the images so doctors can analyse them later. They also use computers to store patient records, which means they can be backed up and are therefore safer than paper records.

**3** Off-the-shelf software is software which can be bought or downloaded straight-away; they are generic applications which anyone can use. Examples include Microsoft Office, Adobe Photoshop and Norton Anti-Virus. The other type is custom-made where the software is specially designed and developed for a particular company. Off-the-shelf is usually cheaper than custom-made because one product can be made and sold to a lot of customers, instead of one product being made for one customer. It is also usually better tested and bug-free, especially if it has been on the market for a while. Off-the-shelf also often has better support and training as it is used by more people and investment can be made in training and publishing reference materials. However, off-the-shelf is not specific to the company and may not carry out tasks exactly as needed. It will also not have the company's logo.

## 70. Unit 1: Practice assessment test

**1** **(a)** **B** FTP

**(b)** Shannon could use CC and BCC to send emails to multiple recipients at the same time. She could also use attachments to send documents with her emails.

**(c)** A risk of email is security as emails are at risk from being infected by viruses.

**2** Simplex = one direction only
Half-duplex = both directions, one at a time
Full duplex = both directions at the same time

**3** **(a)** **D** Commerce

**(b)** Ismail could pay for sponsored links with a search engine which would put their website address at the top of the search results based on specific key words. Also he could use pay-per-click advertising where the website which hosts it gets money each time a user clicks on it.

**4** **(a)**

| Field name | Table name | Type of key |
|---|---|---|
| Patient ID | Patient | Primary key |
| Dentist ID | Dentist | Primary key |
| Patient ID | Dentist | Foreign key |

**(b)**

| Field name | Data type |
|---|---|
| Patient last name | Text |
| Date of birth | Date/time |
| Wears false teeth | Boolean (Yes/No) |
| Telephone number | Text |

**5** **(a)** An online community is a group of people who meet online who usually have similar interests.

**(b)** One example of good netiquette is not to use capital letters because it means shouting.

**6** Two of the following: One risk which Katrina needs to be aware of is computer viruses. These are malicious programs which replicate and can damage or steal data. Anti-virus software can be used to scan for infected files and delete the virus or quarantine the infected files. Another risk is hackers, who are people who try to access areas of a network which are unauthorised. A firewall can protect against hackers because it monitors data going in and out of a network and can prevent hackers from gaining access. Another risk is an opportunist threat, which might be a person who finds an unattended computer that has been logged into a system and they decide to use it to access unauthorised data. This could be prevented with physical security such as locks on the doors, CCTV and ensuring computers are locked or logged off when not in use.

**7** **(a)** VoIP is Voice over Internet Protocol, which is where audio and visual is sent over the internet for teleconferencing. The sender records with a webcam and microphone. The data is encoded with a codec and sent over the internet. At the receiver's end it is decoded with the codec and the receiver can view it on a monitor and hear the sound through speakers or a microphone.

**(b)** Using VoIP means that employees in different branches could have a meeting in their own branches in different countries and do not need to travel, so saving time and money. By using VoIP instead of a text-based communication like email, it is easier to communicate as they can see and hear each other and read facial expressions and body language.

**8**

| File permission | Description |
|---|---|
| Read-only access | Can view the files only |
| Read/Write access | Can view and amend the files but does not enable further actions such as deleting them |
| Full control | Have full access and can perform any action on the files including deleting them |

**9** <a href=www.planets.co.uk/jupiter/><img='jupiter.jpg'> </a>

**10** Angelita could use cloud computing anywhere where there is an internet connection so she could use it at home and at university, and also when she is out elsewhere and can connect to Wi-Fi. Cloud computing usually has automatic backups so she can be confident her data is secure if something happens, such as a file corrupting. As the data is stored on the cloud, she does not need to purchase a computer with a large hard drive therefore she could purchase a cheaper laptop or netbook for working at home, which would be good as she is a student and may not have a lot of money.

However, Angelita should be aware that one risk is reliability because if the internet connection is unavailable or weak then she will not be able to access her files. She is relying on the security of the host company's servers and that it will have up-to-date anti-virus, firewalls and other protections in place. If the host servers crash then the cloud storage will become unavailable and she will not be able to access her files.

**74. Unit 2: Practice assessment test**

**1 (a)** A An input device

**(b)** Sensors monitor where the empty cans are. If they are not in the right place, a robot arm can move it to the correct place. These are controlled by computers which are pre-programmed with instructions.

**(c)** Automated systems do not need much human input, therefore the company can save money by employing fewer staff. (Also robots are much more accurate than humans so the production line may have fewer errors when it is automated.)

**2**

| Variable | Data type |
|---|---|
| Car reg | String |
| Has valid MOT | Boolean |
| Top speed | Integer |

**3 (a)** C Spreadsheet

**(b)**

| | Off-the-shelf | Custom-made |
|---|---|---|
| Benefit 1 | Off-the-shelf software is usually cheaper because it can be developed once rather than for each customer. | Custom-made software will do exactly what is needed by the company paying for it. |
| Benefit 2 | Off-the-shelf software will have better support and training available. | Custom-made software can use the company's logo and colours. |

**4 (a)** High-level languages = Similar to natural language, easier to learn

Low-level languages = Produces a relatively small file size, assembles more quickly into machine code

**(b)**

| Procedural | Event-driven |
|---|---|
| Procedural programs have definite start and end points and the code runs in a sequence. Once it has started running, unless it encounters an error, it will run the same way to the end each time. | Event-driven programs 'listen' for events, such as a mouse click or keyboard press, and carries out the action associated with that event. It is controlled by the user so may run differently each time. |

**5** A programmable digital device is a non-computer device which uses a processor, such as a microwave.

**6** If Stacey chooses a hard disk drive, these are usually cheaper for the same storage capacity as a SSD and can be purchased in larger sizes than a SSD. However a solid state drive is quieter than a HDD and usually more reliable because there are no moving parts. A hard disk drive has a magnetic disk which spins and a read/write head which moves to save and load the data from different sectors whereas a solid state drive uses flash memory to save data by turning transistors on and off to store the data.

**7 (a) 1** Sharing
**2** Communication

**(b)** By using a network the university can share resources; for example, in a computing lab used by learners they can share access to the internet and one printer rather than having to provide an internet connection and printer for each PC. Another benefit is that lecturers can share documents with learners, such as their lecture materials, and learners can submit their work electronically. They can also communicate via email.

**8**

| Binary (base 2) | Denary (base 10) |
|---|---|
| 00000111 | 7 |
| 0101 | 5 |
| 11011011 | 219 |

**9 (a)** Registers, Control unit.

**(b)** The ALU carries out calculations and comparisons.

**(c)** Registers store instructions and results from the ALU.

**10** One function of an operating system is to manage files, allowing users to organise how they store their data by using folders and being able to rename, copy and delete files. Another function is to manage hardware, which uses the components in the device to load programs and use drivers, such as for printers or a graphics card. A third feature is to allocate resources by receiving input such as a mouse click, sending output such as accessing a printer and managing saving to the hard disk drive. Finally, it handles security issues, creating restore points which the user can revert back to, backing up data and controlling access by usernames and passwords.

# Your own notes

# Your own notes

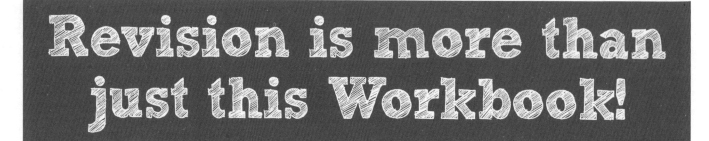

# Revision is more than just this Workbook!

## You can get even more practice on each topic you revise with our full-colour corresponding Revision Guide.

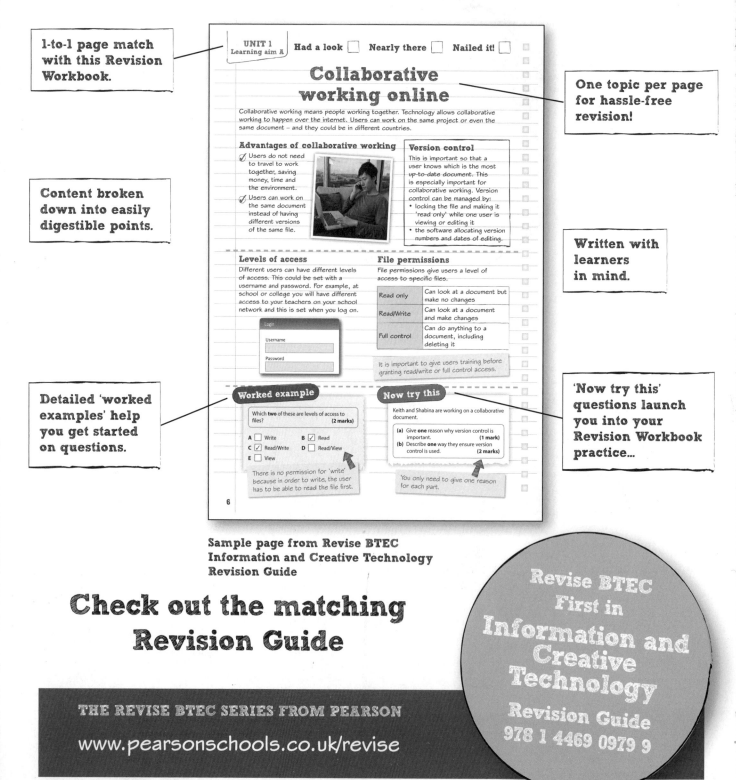

**1-to-1 page match with this Revision Workbook.**

**Content broken down into easily digestible points.**

**Detailed 'worked examples' help you get started on questions.**

**One topic per page for hassle-free revision!**

**Written with learners in mind.**

**'Now try this' questions launch you into your Revision Workbook practice...**

Sample page from Revise BTEC Information and Creative Technology Revision Guide

## Check out the matching Revision Guide

Revise BTEC First in Information and Creative Technology Revision Guide 978 1 4469 0979 9